Galileo

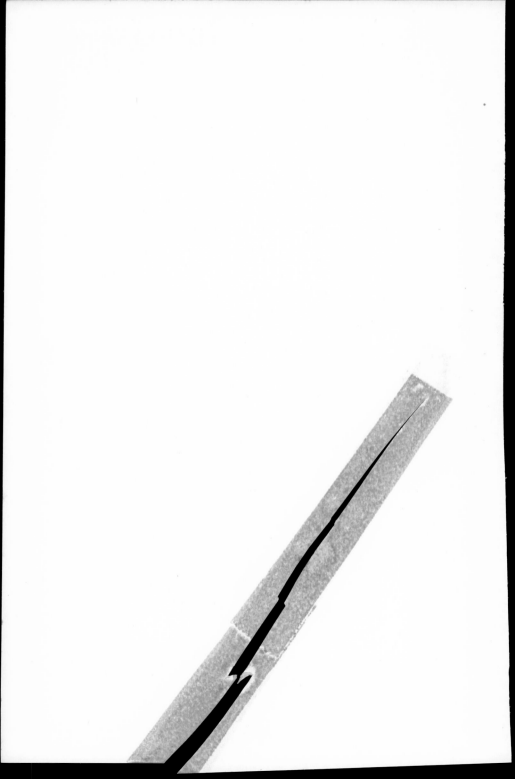

Galileo

BY ARTHUR S. GREGOR

Illustrated by George Giusti

CHARLES SCRIBNER'S SONS

New York

Printed in the United States of America
Library of Congress Catalog Card Number 65-14768

Some years ago I discovered in the heavens many things that had not been seen before our age.
Galileo Galilei

FOR TOM WHO WILL SEE MANY THINGS

Contents

Chapter 1 / In Single Combat

ON A LATE September afternoon in 1573 a boy and his father were fishing in the Arno River. As the sun set, the shadow of the Ponte Vecchio, the Old Bridge, fell on them and the air grew chill.

The Arno flows through the city of Florence in Italy on its way to the sea. It is a muddy, shallow river and one can wait hours for a bite. But nine-year-old Galileo Galilei enjoyed just being there with his father, even though the fish were not biting. The two sat side by side on the rocks for a long while without talking.

Suddenly Galileo flung his arm up and cried, "Look, Father!"

Vincenzio Galilei followed the direction of his son's arm. A faint star glowed in the sky above them.

"The first time so early in the day," Vincenzio said, with wonder in his voice. "The Star of Cassiopeia!"

During the previous year, someone had noticed a tiny

star where none had ever been seen before. Unlike any of the other stars, this one grew brighter night after night.

All over Europe people crowded the streets and squares to stare at the wonder. Was this new star some evil omen? "Mighty kings will perish," warned the fortunetellers and astrologers. "Fire and earthquake will destroy great cities! Plague will sweep the earth!" Horrible rumors quickly spread from country to country.

And now the new star was bright enough to be seen during the day.

Vincenzio removed his pipe from his mouth. "Most people," he said, "believe that the stars have a great influence on mankind. As for me, I think we have enough trouble here on earth without worrying about the heavens."

"Is it really a new star?" Galileo asked.

"Who knows!" said Vincenzio. "Let the professors scratch their heads about it. They say it cannot be a new star. According to the wise Aristotle, each and every star has always been in the heavens. No star, therefore, can be a new star because all the stars were here from the beginning."

Galileo gazed at the new star for some time before he said, "Father, Aristotle was very wise, wasn't he?"

"Indeed, the wisest of all wise men of ancient times. He was the pupil of the Greek philosopher Plato and teacher of Alexander the Great. He knew everything that is to be known."

Galileo slowly repeated, "Everything that is to be

known . . . But Father, how could he have known about things that happened after he died?"

"What do you mean, my son?"

"Well, that pipe you are smoking. Did Aristotle know about that?"

"How could he, my boy? He lived more than three centuries before Christ. Tobacco wasn't discovered until Columbus went to America less than one hundred years ago."

"So Aristotle did not know about tobacco," said Galileo gleefully. "And he didn't know about America. Father, maybe he didn't know about new stars either."

Vincenzio pointed his pipe at his son. "There is one thing, however, *you* do not know, if I may say so."

"What, Father?"

"You have a bite!"

Galileo's float was bobbing wildly up and down.

"Hurrah!" the boy shouted. "At last!"

"Play him, play him," Vincenzio warned. "He's the only fish in the Arno today."

A moment later a tiny fish landed in Galileo's basket.

Vincenzio glanced at the catch. "What a monster!" He laughed. "At least we'll have an excuse for being out so late."

On their way home Galileo and his father crossed the Ponte Vecchio. Then they passed the Uffizi Palace with its magnificent arches that the Grand Duke had built a few years before. As Grand Duke of Tuscany, Cosimo de' Medici ruled over not only Florence but also Siena, Pisa and other nearby cities.

They stopped before a huge stone sculpture in the central square of the city, the Piazza della Signoria. It was a heroic-sized statue of a handsome, curly-haired young man carrying a sling in one hand.

"David," said Vincenzio, "was a shepherd lad only a few years older than you. All by himself he stood up for what he knew was right. He was armed with only a sling and a stone. Yet he defeated the champion of the Philistines."

Galileo loved the story although he had heard it many times. "Go on, Father," he begged.

"Goliath was a giant, six cubits and a span tall. He had a helmet of brass on his head and he wore a coat of mail. The staff of his spear was like a weaver's beam. The head of his spear weighed six hundred shekels of iron.

" 'Choose you a man among you,' he shouted to the Hebrew host. 'And let him come and fight with me in single combat.'

"And when the soldiers heard the words of Goliath, they feared exceedingly. Not one dared to do battle with him. Then David came, bringing cheese and bread for his brothers.

"David went out to meet Goliath and Goliath cursed him saying, 'I will give thy flesh to the fowls of the air and the beasts of the field.' Then did David put his hand in his bag and take out a stone. He slung it and it smote the Philistine in his forehead so that he fell upon his face to the earth. Then David took the Philistine's sword and cut off his head. And when the Philistines saw that their champion was dead, they fled."

Vincenzio turned toward his son. "And who was it that carved this noble statue?"

"Michelangelo, the greatest sculptor in the world," Galileo promptly answered.

"And when did he die?" Vincenzio continued.

Galileo had been waiting for this question.

"The year I was born, 1564."

"In fact," his father pointed out, "the very month, the very week."

"Father," said Galileo as they turned toward home, "you say I am good with my hands. When I grow up, could I be a sculptor like Michelangelo?"

"Yes, Galileo, you could be a sculptor. But like Michelangelo?" He shook his head. "For one Michelangelo, there are a thousand who starve."

"Could I be a musician then, like you?"

"You could be a musician and a good one, I have no doubt. But as your mother says there's not much money in it. I have composed songs and operas. I have written several books on music. But I've never been able to raise a family on music. You see before you not a musician but a wool merchant."

"The best in all Tuscany," said Galileo loyally.

"But not the richest," replied his father.

Vincenzio had opened a shop in the city of Pisa where Galileo had been born. But things had not gone well and he had come to Florence for a fresh start.

As Galileo and his father approached home, the children came running out.

Virginia was crying. "Michel broke my toy. Michel broke my toy."

"I was only playing with it," said Michelangelo, Galileo's younger brother.

"Stop crying," Vincenzio said. "Galileo will make you another."

"Me too, me too," wailed little Livia.

"I'll make new toys for all of you," said Galileo. Even as a young boy, Galileo showed a knack for making mechanical toys and games.

Giulia Galilei came to the door. "Where have you two been?" she scolded.

"I closed the shop early and took the lad fishing," Vincenzio said.

"What a businessman you are, Vincenzio! I send him down to help you out and you take him fishing. Suppose a customer came in. You are acting just the way you did in Pisa. I have heard the women talking in the market. 'What a fine gentleman, that Signore Galilei,' they say. 'Plays the lute so beautifully, sings so well, composes music too.' But nowhere in town, Vincenzio, do I hear anyone saying you are a fine wool merchant."

Vincenzio tried to soothe his wife. "Don't worry, Giulia. Business is bound to pick up."

"Oh, my dear husband, your heart is not in your shop."

"Perhaps, Giulia, I should never have gone into business," said Vincenzio bitterly.

Galileo drew his catch out of his basket. "Look, Mother," he cried. "Look at the monster I caught. Let's all have him for supper."

Giulia began to laugh. "Supper, everyone," she called. "We'll serve Galileo's monster in a thimble."

That night lying in bed Galileo thought of what his father had said: "Perhaps, Giulia, I should never have gone into business." What should his father have done? What should he do when he grew up? If he became a sculptor would he be poor? Would his wife scold? Or should he be an astronomer and find out whether Aristotle was right or not?

His last thought before he fell asleep was of a brave youth with a sling in his hand. Over his head shone a great star. Somehow or other it was he, Galileo Galilei, and not David, who was going forth to slay the giant in single combat.

Chapter 2 / The Warning

GALILEO LONG REMEMBERED the day his father announced he was sending him to school at the monastery of Vallombrosa.

"But Father," Galileo protested, "why can't I stay at home with you and Mother and the children? You are the best teacher in the whole world. Didn't the Grand Duke invite you to the palace to play your own music for his guests? You have taught me to play the lute, to paint and to write poetry. What else do I need to know?"

Vincenzio put his arm affectionately about his son. "Much that I cannot teach you. Some day you will find out how little your father really knew. I hope you will not be too disappointed. When you are older you will go to the university to become a doctor. You will need to know Latin, Greek, Logic and Mathematics, all of which the good monks at Vallombrosa will teach you. Vallombrosa is not too far from Florence and you will be able to come home on holidays."

"Why can't I be a merchant like you?" pleaded Galileo. "I'll work hard; I'll never go fishing and I'll bring home lots of money for all of us."

"My son," said his father earnestly, "you were born for something better than selling wool and yarn all your life. Never forget that you come of one of the noblest families in all Tuscany. You were named for one of your distinguished ancestors, Galileo Galilei, chief magistrate of Florence and a famous physician. It is my desire that you restore our family's position and fortune. At Vallombrosa you will receive the education, not of a tradesman, but of a gentleman. I know that you will do well at the monastery."

His father was right. Galileo quickly got over his homesickness and proved an excellent student. With his agile mind and good memory he became the leader of his class and the favorite of his teachers.

One summer night at Vallombrosa Galileo lay in bed, thinking of the events of the past school year and staring out of the window at the star-swept sky. Whenever he could not sleep, he liked to look up at the stars and wonder about them.

From the far end of the long dormitory he heard the guarded shuffle of a sandal. A glowing lantern floated toward him. It must be young Brother Paolo on his nightly rounds. Galileo smiled, remembering the astonishment on Brother Paolo's face earlier that day.

In the afternoon the boys had been gathered in a circle outside the bell tower. Galileo stood in the middle of the circle whirling about his head a long net holding three eggs.

"Faster! Faster!" cried the boys. "Do it faster!"

Encouraged by their cries, Galileo spun around like a swift top, the net whirring above him.

Suddenly Brother Paolo appeared. "What's happening here?"

"Cooking eggs," the boys yelled, dancing up and down with excitement. "Galileo's cooking eggs!"

"Stop the nonsense at once!" Brother Paolo demanded.

At that moment the net gave way and the eggs flew directly at Brother Paolo. He dropped to the ground in the nick of time and the eggs splattered against the wall of the bell tower. The boys turned and ran. But before the dizzy, perspiring Galileo could get away, Brother Paolo had grabbed him by the collar.

"My experiment!" cried Galileo "My Babylonian experiment!"

"What experiment? What Babylonians?"

Galileo struggled to catch his breath. "It all started in Greek class when Father Orsini translated the story by Suidas. It tells about the way the ancient Babylonians cooked their eggs."

"Don't tell me they whirled them about their heads!"

"Well, that's what the story says. You can ask Father Orsini. So after class we began to argue back and forth. Some said the eggs would be hard-boiled. Some said they would be only soft-boiled; still others said they would not cook at all."

"What did you say?"

"I said that instead of arguing we ought to find out for ourselves. So another dispute started. Some held we should look up other writers to see what they said. Still others held we ought to try it out for ourselves."

Brother Paolo tried to look stern. "So you tried it out and you now see the result. Scrambled eggs!"

"But Brother Paolo, I remembered the time I rode a swift horse and the wind made me feel not hotter but cooler. I reasoned, therefore, that the eggs should become not warmer but cooler. 'Perhaps,' I said to myself, 'the Babylonians who lived so long ago are in error. To judge the truth once and for all, I will try an experiment. I will find out for myself.' Is there anything wrong in that, Brother?"

Brother Paolo smiled. "Who knows what could happen because a boy of thirteen once whirled an egg about his head? If Suidas be in error, let other and more learned writers prove him wrong. Leave such solemn matters to your elders. Now go and get yourself scrubbed up after all this foolish exertion. And don't forget the wall."

The lantern came closer and then hung suspended over Galileo's bed.

"Still cooking eggs?" a voice whispered.

"No, Brother, I was thinking."

Brother Paolo sat down by the side of the bed. "Of what, my boy?"

"Oh—just things. Brother Paolo, remember the star a few years ago in the Constellation Cassiopeia that grew brighter and brighter until you could see it during the day?"

"And then began to fade and finally disappeared altogether. Yes, I remember, Galileo."

"Brother Paolo, where did it go?"

"Some day, you may know, Galileo, especially if you continue to apply yourself to your books. There the answers are set down for all time. Just yesterday I heard Father Orsini say no student at Vallombrosa excels you in industry and eagerness for knowledge. You will become a great scholar, perhaps another Archimedes, he says. Who knows? That is, if you go to sleep at once."

But Brother Paolo made no effort to leave. He and Galileo stared at the heavens as though spellbound. Several meteors flared across the sky and then were snuffed out in the darkness.

"I have been watching the Great Dipper," Galileo said at last, "and the other constellations. They all move across the sky from east to west just as the sun does."

"A good observation," said Brother Paolo. "Aristotle teaches that all the heavenly spheres turn in the same direction. In the very center of the universe, our globe, the home of man, hangs suspended, motionless in the void. Sur-

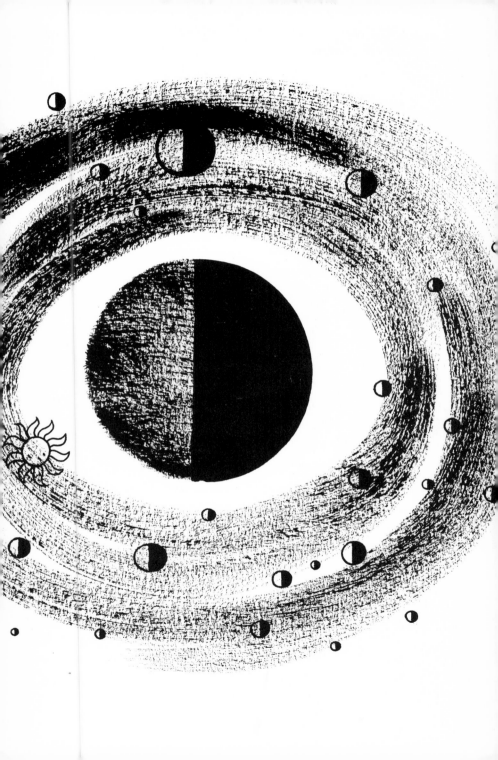

rounding the earth are the crystal spheres holding the moon, the sun, the planets and the stars. Each of them turns about the stationary earth once every twenty-four hours.

"On earth weather and seasons change. Planets, animals and men are born, they grow, and they die. Nothing is permanent. But in the sky all is perfect and everlastingly the same. The heavenly bodies wondrously smooth and round, move in the most perfect figure, the circle, and in the most perfect direction, from east to west."

"And beyond the last sphere of the stars, Brother Paolo, what is there?"

"The realm of the angels," said Brother Paolo, "whose task it is to move the heavenly spheres about the earth."

Far in the east a faint glow appeared and the stars began to fade. The last meteor of the night plunged through the sky and disappeared.

"Brother Paolo, the shooting stars, can they go through the crystal spheres?"

"Questions, questions, questions! Be not so impatient. The vast sea of knowledge is not crossed in a single day, my boy. Sleep now before cock crow shakes you out of bed."

Brother Paolo softly intoned the 19th Psalm:

The heavens declare the glory of God,
*   and the firmament showeth his handiwork.*
Day unto day uttereth speech,
*   and night unto night showeth knowledge.*
There is no speech nor language,
*   where their voice is not heard.*

Their line is gone out through all the earth,
    and their words to the end of the world.
In them hath he set a tabernacle for the sun,
    which is as a bridegroom coming out of his chamber,
    and rejoiceth as a strong man to run a race.
His going forth is from the end of heaven,
    and his circuit unto the ends of it. . . .

Galileo turned on his side, drawing his cover over his shoulder. How comforting it was to know that he lived in the immovable center of the universe with God and his angels to look after him and the crystal spheres to circle forever about him.

Slowly the lantern disappeared down the long, dark corridor.

One day toward the end of his last year at Vallombrosa, Galileo was summoned to the study of the abbot. Father Orsini was very old and his skin, stretched taut about his cheekbones, was pale white and thin.

His voice quavered as he spoke. "My eyes fail me," he said. "Come here, my son. Sit in the light. So you have red hair. A high forehead, wide-apart, alert brown eyes, a broad nose, sturdy chin, strong shoulders, barrel chest. You are well-knit, my lad, if not exactly handsome. How old are you now? Sixteen? Well, I have your father's letter. He informs me you are going to study medicine. We have therefore arranged for you to enter the University of Pisa which has one of the best medical schools in Europe. The city should not be altogether strange to you since it was your birthplace."

"But, Father, where will the money come from? My family has hardly enough to send me here."

"Do not worry," said Father Orsini. "In Pisa you will live with your kinsman, Muzio Tedaldi. And your father has already applied for one of the scholarships given by the Grand Duke to needy students. We will recommend you to him highly."

"I am most grateful," Galileo said very quietly.

Father Orsini looked at him questioningly. "You hardly seem very happy."

"I love my father," said Galileo. "I know what he has sacrificed for me and I will do whatever he wishes. But—"

Father Orsini put his wrinkled hand on Galileo's. "Go on, my son."

"I really don't know what I want to be. When I was very young, I wanted to be an artist and sculpt statues like Michelangelo. Once I wanted to work in my father's shop but he insisted I receive the education of a gentleman. Sometimes I can gaze at the heavens hour after hour as though I'm held by some mysterious power. Strange thoughts crowd my mind and I cannot sleep. The other night I was thinking of how the sun completes a circle about the earth every twenty-four hours. Thus, according to the ancient astronomers, we have night and day. Ptolemy tells us that the orbit of the sun about the earth is almost twenty million miles. How can the sun, I ask myself, travel such a distance in twenty-four hours? Only by moving at a most wondrous speed. The thought then comes to me: Why then is not the sun shattered to bits?"

Father Orsini began to laugh. "Such a notion: the sun shattering! How else do we get night and day if the sun did not go about the earth? Would you have the earth spin about like some silly child, first presenting its face and then its backside to the sun? Besides, it's all set forth in Holy Writ. It is the sun that moves, not the earth.

"Put such thoughts away, my son. They are the instrument of the Evil One. What mad ideas we hear nowadays. They all began when Christopher Columbus sailed to the New World."

In his excitement Father Orsini raised his voice. "All these explorations, discoveries, inventions, heresies! Magellan circling the globe and losing his fool head. Serves him right! Leonardo da Vinci dabbling with flying machines instead of tending to his sacred art! The Polish stargazer Copernicus devising new designs for the universe, not content to leave Ptolemy alone. Spirit of inquiry, they call it. Rubbish, I say!"

The old man paused to catch his breath and rest for a moment.

"I have high hopes for you, my son. But I must solemnly warn you not to give way to these modern ideas. At the university the professors do not take kindly to flights of fancy. Listen, but do not question. Cultivate your memory but curb your imagination. Speak to confirm not to deny what the ancients have taught. Above all else, keep firm your faith in Aristotle and the Church Fathers.

"Kneel, Galileo Galilei. I am an old man and my eyes grow dim. Yet it sometimes seems to me that they can penetrate the veil of the future. I foresee for you much sorrow and suffering. Yet one day you will bring to your family more honor and fame than ever did the noble ancestor for whom you were named. And now my blessing."

Chapter 3 / The Pendulum

THE LEANING TOWER of Pisa looked as though one good push would topple it over. Almost from the day it was completed, it had started to sink into the soft earth. And now it stood, tilted to one side, as it had for over two hundred years.

Galileo gave it a wide berth as he passed by. Small boys were known to drop things down on the heads of unsuspecting students. He swung across the green lawn and entered the great white cathedral.

Galileo sank to his knees and tried to pray. But the words would not come. In his mind, instead, a harsh voice kept repeating, "Hold your tongue! Hold your tongue, young man!"

He had been at the university for over a year now and things were not going well. Despite Father Orsini's recommendation to the Grand Duke, the scholarship had never come through. Galileo's father had been forced to spend his last penny to keep him at school. Were it not for Uncle Muzio, he would not have a roof over his head.

Worse still, his studies made no sense to him. Medicine was not a science but a hocus-pocus of old wives' tales and guesswork. You listened to the professor drone on hour after hour. Then you memorized lists of rules made up by physicians of ancient times, such as Hippocrates and Galen. But you never had a chance to find out whether these rules helped sick people.

The other students did not seem to mind. After class, their pockets clinking with coins, they rushed down to the taverns to sing and drink, while Galileo walked home alone.

"Sir," Galileo had asked one day in class, "how do we know that the heart draws air into the blood vessels?"

Galileo's classmates, busily scribbling into their notebooks, looked up, annoyed. If the learned Professor Cesalpino says so, should that not be enough for anyone?

Professor Cesalpino raised his eyes from the heavy book before him and frowned. "You are Galileo Galilei, aren't you?"

"Yes, sir."

"You have been at the medical school for one year, haven't you?"

"Yes, sir."

"Suppose then, young man, you hold your tongue until you know enough to ask intelligent questions. Please be seated."

But Galileo did not sit down. "Sir, please, may I most respectfully ask how we know that—"

Professor Cesalpino spluttered, "How do we know! How do we know! We know because Galen says so. In case you should still be unaware of who Galen was, he was the most famous doctor of Roman times. He was also personal physician to Emperor Marcus Aurelius. Though Galen died thirteen hundred years ago, doctors have accepted his authority ever since. I trust his references are satisfactory to you.

"And now, gentlemen, unless the learned Doctor Galilei has some objection, class dismissed!"

And so it had gone, week after week. Galileo had a way of asking questions that disturbed his teachers. And yet he never received a satisfactory answer.

Now, in the darkened cathedral, Galileo asked himself, "Is there something wrong with me? Why should I be so different from the others? They accept everything they hear. To them I am just a troublemaker. Galileo the Wrangler, that's what they call me. Always wrangling and arguing! If my teachers would only offer some real proof of what they say! If there were only some way of testing—"

Galileo's eye was caught by one of the great lamps that hung from the cathedral ceiling by a long bronze chain. The sexton had opened a side door, letting in a gust of wind. One . . . two . . . three . . . four . . . one . . . two . . . three . . . four . . . one . . . As Galileo counted, the lamp swung to and fro in a wide arc. Then the door closed and each swing grew shorter. But each swing, long or short, seemed to take the same length of time.

If only he had some way of timing the swings. His fingers reached for his pulse. The lamp swung in ever shorter arcs. And yet for every swing he counted the same number of pulse beats. It was true. Each swing, no matter what its distance, was taking exactly the same time.

Galileo felt a strange sense of excitement; it was as though he were doing something real for the first time since coming to Pisa. He knew what the books had to say. "The longer the swing, the longer the time; the shorter the swing, the shorter the time."

But the great lamp in the cathedral at Pisa seemed to contradict the rule. Was there something odd about this lamp? Or were the old authorities wrong? He must test out his idea at once. He would set up a pendulum arrangement at home and measure the time again and again. If he could only be right! Then all those who had called him names in the past, all those who had jeered at him for asking questions—

He ran home through the darkened streets and dashed upstairs.

"Is that you, Galileo?" Muzio called. "Kept after school for talking back to your professors, I'll wager."

But Galileo did not reply. He rummaged around his tiny attic bedroom that also served as a laboratory and study. Then he half-slid, half-flew downstairs.

"Look, Uncle!" he cried.

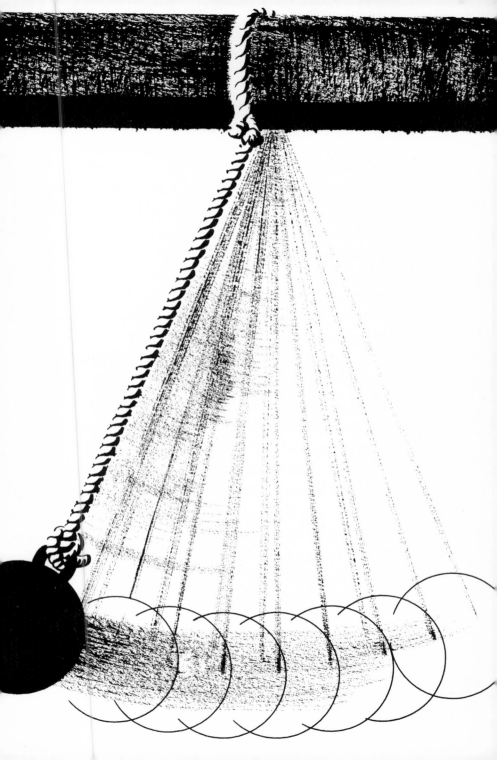

He looped a long cord around a ceiling beam and attached an iron weight to the loose end. Then he pulled the weight toward him and let go. Back and forth it rocked. And then gradually the arcs grew shorter.

"Well, what do you see?" asked Galileo.

"An exercise for strengthening the eye muscles," said Muzio who loved to tease his young relative.

"Oh, stop joking," Galileo pleaded. "Just tell me what is happening."

"The swings are getting shorter."

"Right! Now which takes longer, the short swing or the long swing?"

"Do you take me for a fool? The long swing, of course. Now if you'll be good enough to remove this gallows before someone hangs himself."

"Just a moment now, Uncle. The long swing you say! How do you know?"

"Stands to reason, my young philosopher. Short swing, short time; long swing, long time. Any fool knows that."

"Well," said Galileo, smiling broadly, "who knows but you may be right. But let's try, shall we? I start the pendulum going again and you time it with your pulse. Ready, Uncle? Go!"

"One . . . two . . . three . . . one . . . two . . . three . . . one . . ." Muzio murmured.

Suddenly he cried out in amazement, "Each swing takes the same time!"

"How do you explain that?"

Muzio's eyes twinkled. "Something wrong with my pulse. Doesn't Aristotle say—"

"Aristotle be hanged!" Galileo exploded. "For over a thousand years men have been repeating: Aristotle said! Ptolemy said! Hippocrates said! Galen said! Hasn't anybody ever taken the trouble to find out whether what they said was true?"

"All right," said the practical Muzio. "Suppose a pendulum does swing in equal time no matter the length of the arc. What's the good of it?"

"I've thought of that, too," said Galileo. "Let me ask you: What is the first thing a doctor does when he sees a patient?"

"Figures out how much he'll overcharge."

"Wrong," said Galileo. "He takes his patient's pulse. But how does he time the pulse?"

"Guesswork for the most part,'" Muzio replied.

"Exactly, Uncle. Well, here is a way to remove the guesswork. Let me draw a picture for you. Here is a pendulum, just a weight at the end of a string. Here is a scale. The doctor sets the pendulum going and takes the patient's pulse. Then he shortens the string until each swing keeps time with the pulse beat. Finally he takes a reading from the scale that tells him whether the pulse is normal, rapid or slow."

Muzio was serious for once. "Galileo," he said, "until the day that more accurate ways of telling time are invented, men will continue to thank you. Now if you are to make any money with this marvelous little invention, what about a good name. Let's see: pulsitimer? pulsometer? pulsifier? I've got it: pulsilogia!"

And pulsilogia it was.

Muzio was right. The pusilogia became the standard method of taking the pulse until the invention of reliable clocks and watches many years later. Galileo, however, never made any money on it. Every doctor as soon as he heard of the new device simply made one for himself.

Even Professor Cesalpino was impressed. "Not bad, my boy, not bad," he said to Galileo. "You have a head on your shoulders. You'll go a long way, that is if you learn to curb your tongue. Now haven't I heard that your family is having a hard time keeping you in school? A hint from me to the university officials could be most helpful at this time."

Galileo knew just what Professor Cesalpino meant. He was again applying for a free scholarship. A word from Professor Cesalpino and his worries would be over.

A fierce rage swept through Galileo. He was a far better student than any of the pampered blockheads that sat in class with him and absorbed everything like sponges. While they idled their time away in the taverns, he, Galileo Galilei, whose ancestors had dined with princes, went about in rags, living off the charity of a distant kinsman.

Professor Cesalpino went on. "No doubt you think us very old-fashioned. I was impatient, too, at your age. I had my dreams. I wondered also. But I quickly learned to keep my thoughts to myself. Don't challenge the ancient authorities, Galileo. Come over to our side. Great rewards can be yours."

Galileo struggled to control himself. "Professor Cesalpino," he replied, "long ago my father taught me that the truth is not always within the covers of the oldest book on the shelf. I cannot believe simply because others have believed. What the old authorities have said about the motion of the pendulum was false. Shall I, like a parrot, repeat what they said? Or shall I experiment and find out for myself? I shall ask questions as long as I live. I shall never cease to wonder."

"Bravissimo!" cried Professor Cesalpino. "Brave words, indeed!"

But his eyes were cold and hard.

Chapter 4 / The Failure

GALILEO SPENT THREE long, unhappy years at Pisa, years in which he doubted more and more whether he would ever become a doctor.

One late spring afternoon he was walking home from class so deep in thought he was unaware of the driving rain that had soaked through his ragged cloak. Again and again he kept saying to himself, "But if not a doctor, what then? I'm fit for nothing else. I paint, I sing, I read Latin and Greek, I play the lute. Fine talents for a gentleman but not for earning a living. I have another gift, I certainly can annoy my teachers. Much good that has ever done me!"

Turning in under the archway of his kinsman's house, he recalled his father's last letter:

"Study hard and honor your professors, even if they are donkeys. You are at school not to argue but to get your degree. Business is no worse than usual which means it's terrible. Tell Muzio I'll pay for your board when a little money comes into the shop. As you can imagine all the talk at home is about getting your sister Virginia married off. But who will have the daughter of a poor man without a marriage gift? Unless we can raise the money for her dowry, she'll end up in a convent. Your little brother Michelangelo is beginning to show great promise. I dream of the day when he is court musician to a great prince and you, my eldest, are a famous doctor. As for your mother, she scolds and scolds, says I'm too weak to spend so much time in the shop. Nonsense, I tell her, I may have a little ache here and there but that's all. I almost forgot to tell you. Ostilio Ricci has promised to look . . ."

Suddenly Galileo heard his uncle's voice:

"Where have you been so long?" Muzio cried, rushing to the door. "Just one hour ago, a fine carriage at the door with the coat of arms of the Grand Duke; two footmen, very grand; four white horses, very grand; fancy gentleman within, with a little pointed grey beard and a long staff, also very grand!

"Now who can be calling on poor Muzio Tedaldi? Lost his way in the rain, no doubt! Nevertheless, I run down, I greet him, I bow low. Galileo, you should have seen me.

"But what does he say? 'Is this the home of the respected gentleman Muzio Tedaldi?' His very words, so help me.

" 'Indeed,' says I. 'Indeed it is. This is his humble home.'

" 'Have I the honor of addressing Signore Tedaldi?' says he.

" 'Your worship,' says I, 'it is indeed Signore Tedaldi you have the honor of addressing.'

" 'I have some reason to believe,' says he, 'you know the person I am looking for.' "

Muzio was enjoying his story. "Now, Galileo, you're a smart one. Three guesses. Who is the grand gentleman looking for?"

"Uncle," cried Galileo. "For once be serious. Hurry with your story."

"But I am hurrying," said Muzio, pretending to be hurt. "The long and short of it is that the gentleman is looking for you."

"What did you say?"

" 'Begging his lordship's pardon,' I said, 'my dear kinsman Galileo, is at this very moment in class at the university, a quiet, well-mannered, most respectful and shy youth, a never-ending joy to his teachers and the inventor of a quaint device to measure the human pulse of which the very grand gentleman has no doubt heard.'

"The gentleman listens with marked attention to my every word, unlike a certain young relative of mine. And then, when I am at last quite out of breath for singing your praises, he says, 'When this remarkable kinsman of yours returns, tell him Ostilio Ricci called and awaits him at the Ducal Palace this afternoon.'

"Whereupon the gentleman vanishes into the coach, a crack of the whip and he's gone. And if you still think that Muzio Tedaldi, Respected Gentleman, is joking, look at the marks of his wheels in the mud. Galileo, please, at once, who is Ostilio Ricci?"

"Mathematician at the court of the Grand Duke," said Galileo, "and an old school friend of my father. Whenever Grand Duke Ferdinand comes here from Florence he takes Ostilio along to lecture to the young princes and the court pages."

"Then, off with these wet clothes and into your Sunday best. There is the sun coming out, a good sign."

"Sunday best!" Galileo exclaimed. "I haven't a garment that isn't worn through."

"Then take this," Muzio said, beginning to strip off his doublet. "You can't lose a moment."

When Galileo entered the Ducal Palace later that afternoon, he was led into an anteroom. Signore Ricci was giving his daily lesson. Would the young gentleman be good enough to wait?

Galileo heard Ostilio's voice coming from a room close by and he began to listen attentively. Everything Ricci said to his class was clear and reasonable. Every statement he made grew step by step. Here was no guesswork or repeating of ancient writers. One answered Ostilio's questions with actual proof, not with what one found in a book.

How different from the nonsense Galileo had been forced to listen to all these years. Surely Ostilio Ricci was the greatest teacher in the world and mathematics the most noble subject.

At last Galileo knew what he wanted for himself. He

would be an explorer of nature—the earth, the sky, the stars, liquids, energy, motion. He would ask questions of them all and discover the answers with the help of mathematics.

He recalled the method by which he had worked out the law of the pendulum. First one observes carefully, the way he had studied the movement of the lamp in the cathedral. Then one draws up a hypothesis or guess: a pendulum seems to swing in equal time no matter the length of each swing. Then one tests the hypothesis by trying a number of experiments, as he had done at home that night. Finally, after checking and rechecking the results, one comes to a conclusion and draws up a law about it.

If this new way of finding the truth could be used to understand the motion of the pendulum, why, Galileo thought to himself, couldn't it be used to solve a thousand other mysteries of nature. But first he would have to learn a great deal about mathematics.

Ostilio was hardly out of his classroom before Galileo was pleading with him. "Professor Ricci, may I join your class?"

"Certainly," said Ostilio, "but your father, I must tell you, will not be happy. He talks of nothing but the day you will begin to practice medicine in Florence."

"I know, Professor Ricci, but my mind is made up. I can no longer continue what I have been doing."

Soon after, Galileo gave up his classes in medicine at the university and turned to the study of mathematics and science. But his troubles were not over. "A brilliant young man," his professors said, "but he doesn't have to act as though he knows more than we do."

Again Galileo asked Grand Duke Ferdinand for a scholarship and again he was refused. His father could no longer keep him at school. In the summer of 1585 Galileo left Pisa without graduating.

He was going home, a failure. His mother would scold and accuse him of throwing away his father's hard-earned money. His father would say nothing but his silence would be more difficult to bear than his mother's remarks.

Galileo was twenty-one years old, an age when young men of his day were already out in the world earning their own living, and still he had to be supported by his family. "Come what may," he said to himself, "I will be a mathematician."

As the rough carriage jounced over the dusty road, he turned back to take a last look at Pisa. The cathedral had disappeared to the right and all he could see was the top of the Leaning Tower over the flat meadows.

I will never see it again, Galileo thought bitterly. He did not know how wrong he was.

Chapter 5 / Good News

GIULIA GALILEI'S FACE fell as she entered her kitchen. It was filled with jars, scales and various kinds of hardware.

"Mother," said Galileo proudly, "you are going to be the first to see this experiment."

"What have you done to my lovely kitchen!" Giulia cried.

"I haven't any place else to work," said Galileo. "Michel sleeps so late."

"Do you envy him his rest? He must be worn out after all his practicing, poor child. Now get this mess out of here so that I can prepare your father's lunch. You should be with him in the shop instead of puttering around here."

"But Mother, I've got a new invention. Aren't you going to look at it?"

"Invention!" Giulia's voice rose. "What good have your inventions ever done us? How much did you make on that pulse-something-or-other? Twenty-five years of age and still unable to earn a living! Twenty-five years of age and still playing with children's toys!"

Galileo flushed a deep red. He understood his mother's feelings only too well. He had been home for four years and he had been unable to find regular work. One after the other, the universities of Padua, Bologna, and Florence had turned him down. Wherever he went, his reputation as a troublemaker had gone ahead of him. In desperation he had even thought of moving to a Far Eastern country where he would be unknown.

In the meantime he taught a few private pupils, in Florence and in the neighboring city of Siena, that Ostilio Ricci sent to him. But as Giulia said, he did not earn enough to feed a mouse. He continued his studies by himself, taking as his model Archimedes, the famous scientist of ancient times. Cut off from schools and teachers, Galileo began the research that would finally lead the world into the modern age of science. To his mother, however, he was a ne'er-do-well, living off the charity of an aging and sick father.

Galileo tried to soothe Giulia. "This time I have an idea that will bring us lots of money. Now take that bracelet you're wearing. Would you say it's pure gold?"

"Certainly!" replied Giulia. "Your father gave it to me when we were married."

"But can you be positive? Suppose, just suppose, the goldsmith had put a bit of silver into it. I have here a device that will quickly tell you just what it is made of. Here, let me test it for you."

Giulia drew back and put her hand over the bracelet. "A fine invention," she said, "stirring up suspicion in people's minds. Now I won't sleep for thinking about it."

She spied her husband coming in the door.

"Do you hear, Vincenzio? Galileo dares to say my bracelet is not pure gold."

"Father, all I did was to offer to test it in my new balance. I think I've improved on Archimedes."

"Archimedes?" Vincenzio looked surprised. "Wasn't it he who set fire to the entire Roman fleet off Syracuse, by using huge concave mirrors to concentrate the sun's rays on their sails?"

Galileo smiled. "A tale which may or may not be true. But my idea comes from the story of King Hiero's new crown. His goldsmith had sworn the crown was pure gold, but how could the king be certain? Only one man, the great Archimedes, mathematician and scientist, could ease his mind.

" 'Discover,' cried the king, 'what is in this new crown of mine but without so much as scratching it.'

" 'The crown certainly looks like pure gold,' Archimedes said to himself. 'But suppose there is a bit of silver in it. How do you tell? The appearance would not change. But then, what about the weight? Silver weighs far less than an equal volume of gold. Therefore if the crown contained any silver, it would weigh less than an equal volume of pure gold. Here's the problem then: How do you go about measuring the volume of an irregularly shaped object such as this crown?

"In the morning, after a sleepless night, Archimedes stepped into his bath without noticing that the water was up to the brim. As he lay down, the water overflowed. Archimedes began to ask himself questions: 'How much overflowed? Would it not be equal in volume to the space my body occupies in the water? Were I completely under the water would it be equal to the volume of my entire body?'

"Suddenly, so the story goes, Archimedes shouted, *'Eureka!'* meaning, *I have found my answer*, snatched his towel, dashed headlong out of the house and headed for the palace.

"He had found a way of measuring the volume of an irregular object. All he had to do was place it in water. The volume of the water that overflowed would equal the volume of the object.

"In the king's presence Archimedes prepared a mass of gold that weighed as much as the crown. He dropped the gold into a jar filled with water and carefully measured the volume that overflowed. In similar manner he dropped the crown into a jar and measured the overflow also. Had the crown been pure gold the volumes should have been exactly the same. But alas, the crown caused more water to overflow than did the mass of gold. The goldsmith had tricked his king."

"What happened to him then?" asked Giulia, who had followed the story with great interest.

"We are not told," said Galileo. "But the story made

me wonder whether I could find an even better way of testing metals. We all know that objects weigh less in water than they do in air. The loss of weight is equal to the weight of the water that overflows. This led me to think that by weighing whatever I was testing in and out of water, I could discover what it was made of.

"I have here what I call a hydrostatic balance. Suppose Mother allowed me to test her bracelet. We'd weigh it in water and in air. Then a quick reading on this balance would tell just how much gold and silver it contained."

"There, Giulia," Vincenzio said, "you see he meant no harm."

At the mention of the bracelet, all of Giulia's anger returned.

"Always taking his side," she cried, beginning to sob. "Some day I'll be a widow with two marriageable daughters and who will take care of me? You sent him to school to be a doctor and he insults every professor. Instead of getting a job, he buries his head in Archimedes all day long. And now look at my kitchen!"

Vincenzio sat down wearily in his chair.

"Giulia," he said slowly, "you know I've had my dreams for Galileo too. In the end, however, he'll have to find his own way. He may never be rich but I think he will find great joy in his work. Galileo, my son, I've never told you, but there was a time when I also thought of becoming a mathematician."

"Why didn't you, Father?"

"Because he had a family to support," Giulia snapped.

There was a knock on the open door but in the heat of the argument none of them heard it.

Giulia turned angrily on her husband. "He'd be a doctor today if you hadn't sent him to that very fancy gentleman friend of yours who stuffed his head with algebra and geometry. And what of all the fine promises he made to speak to the Grand Duke about getting your son a job at one of the universities? I don't see him coming around here any longer, what was his name?"

"Ostilio Ricci, Signora. I knocked but no one answered."

Giulia's mouth opened wide but she quickly recovered herself.

"Professor Ricci, what a pleasure!" She curtseyed low. "We were just talking about you."

"Pardon me for breaking in on you so suddenly, but I have some welcome news," Ostilio said.

"I am happy to tell you that the Grand Duke has given Galileo a full professorship in mathematics at the University of Pisa. It is a most unusual honor for one so young."

Vincenzio was the first to recover himself. He rushed over to Ostilio and wrapped his arms tightly about him. "Old friend," he said, "how can we ever thank you enough."

"Pisa!" cried Galileo. "What will my old teachers think?"

Giulia kissed her son proudly. *"Professor* Galilei," she said, "aren't you going to test my bracelet?"

Chapter 6 / The Leaning Tower

THE STORY OF Galileo and the Leaning Tower spread like wildfire through the University of Pisa. It was discussed in the classrooms, in the taverns and in the student eating places. No one said he had actually seen the experiment, but everyone claimed he knew someone who had been there.

The class buzzed with excitement long before Professor Galilei arrived. He was known to do unusual things but this was the strangest he had ever done, that is, if he had really done it. Galileo had come to the university as a teacher two years before. From the day of his arrival he had been the center of argument and talk.

"His manners certainly haven't improved since his student days," his fellow professors said. "He's more set in his ways than ever. He respects neither our age nor our honors. By what right does he poke fun at our caps and gowns? We've worn them not only in class but in the halls and in the streets for hundreds of years. You'd think that with age he would have grown a little more serious, but he's as difficult as ever. And to think he got his position without a degree!

"Now, this strange story. It is going to make our university the laughing stock of Europe. Professor Cesalpino, were you there when he climbed to the top of the Leaning Tower?"

"No, Professor Santucci. What about you, Professor Mazzoni?"

"Not I. I'm more interested in the material Professor Galilei has on the platform, that long wooden beam with the groove down the middle, the bucket of water and the scales."

"Well, Professor Mazzoni, you ought to know what it is all about. You're a friend of his. But here comes our famous experimenter now."

Galileo strode up to the platform and faced his class. In the time he had been teaching at Pisa he had become more confident and poised. He had grown a full red beard and he looked older than his twenty-seven years.

"Good morning, gentlemen," he said in a clear voice that carried to all corners of the lecture room. "We seem to have increased in size since we met last week. Welcome to all our famous visitors—Professor Santucci, the great expert on Aristotle, my good friend Professor Mazzoni and Professor Cesalpino whom I knew as a student in medical school.

"When I said last week I was going to talk about falling bodies, I never thought the topic would interest so many well-known people. Neither did I think it would give rise to an odd story. According to this tale, a certain red-bearded professor climbed the Leaning Tower lugging a ten-pound weight under one arm and a one-hundred-pound weight under the other.

"After struggling breathlessly to the top, he immediately tossed both weights over the side, strange conduct I must say, even for a college professor. He is supposed to have done so to see if they would strike the ground at the same time. Gentlemen, let me tell you at once I did no such thing. In the first place I doubt I have the strength to lug one hundred and ten pounds to the top of the Leaning Tower. In the second place I am a mathematician, not a circus performer.

"Suppose I had done such an experiment. What would it prove? Nothing! It would be over before you knew what it was all about. You could not measure the speed at which the weights dropped. You could not tell whether they sped up as they fell or held a regular rate of speed throughout their fall. Then too, some would say the experiment was meaningless because the weights did not fall far enough.

"I too believe that such an experiment would tell us little. We must find the kind of experiment in which the results can be measured with mathematical accuracy.

"Before we try to set up such an experiment let us review what the ancients tell us about falling bodies. Aristotle teaches that objects fall because they tend toward their natural place which is the center of the universe. According

to Aristotle, the center of the universe is the earth itself so
that objects will seek the ground as a child its mother's arms.

"The ancients seem to be interested in why things fall.
We, however, are interested in *how* they fall. We want to
find out just what happens to them as they fall and if possible, measure the speed of their fall.

"Now let us return to the Leaning Tower and the
experiment I did not do. Suppose I had dropped two objects
of different weights. Which would you say should reach the
ground first. Signore Corsi, my honest pupil, what would you
say?"

"Certainly, Professor Galilei, the heavier weight."

"And if one weight were ten times heavier than the
other?"

"Then, sir, such a weight will reach the earth in one-
tenth the time it takes the lighter."

"Well said, my good Corsi. Then you have tried the
experiment?"

"No, sir."

"Oh, I'm sorry. But surely you have some good reason,
shall we say, some *weighty* reason for your belief."

"Well, sir, I have read it in our master Aristotle. Besides, sir, it is good common sense. The . . ."

" . . . heavier the weight, the faster the fall?"

"That's right, sir."

"Thank you, Corsi. And now, gentlemen, we have
heard the good common sense of our friend here, let us turn
to the simple material I have on this platform. You see be-

fore you a plank of wood twenty feet long and one foot wide. Down the center runs a straight channel the width of one finger which I have smoothed and polished with great care and lined with the finest glazed leather. Now I turn this plank into an inclined plane by lifting one end off the ground. So!

"Here I have a finely polished bronze ball and here another of just the same size but much lighter, being made of cork. With such simple materials and apparatus we shall try to uncover some of the fundamental laws of nature.

"Now, good Corsi, if you will please come forward, in just one moment I am going to ask you to roll both balls down the plank. I know you are all thinking: What has a ball rolling down a slope to do with a weight falling? Just this. A ball rolling down a slope behaves very much like a weight in a free fall. We are slowing down a fall so that we can actually see what is happening.

"If you will look in this direction, gentlemen. Here you see a little thing of my own invention, a water clock, so simple that even a small child can make it for himself. It consists of an ordinary bucket of water near the bottom of which is a tiny hole and a spigot. When Corsi lets the ball go, I will open the spigot and a very fine thread of water will squirt into this cup. The moment the ball reaches the end of the plank I close the spigot and I weigh the cup of water on this very sensitive scale. Since no one has as yet invented a good mechanical clock, we will measure time by weighing the water that has flowed out of the bucket.

"Are we ready for our experiment? Excellent! We'll time the cork ball, first. But before we start, good Corsi, which ball will take the longer time?"

"The cork ball, sir."

"Well, we'll see, we'll see. When I say, 'Go,' you release the ball and I will open the spigot. Go!

"Well done, good Corsi. And now let us do the same with the bronze ball. . . . All right, here are two cups of water. Doesn't each seem to hold the same amount of water? But let us not rely on our eyes alone. Place each cup on the scale. Ah, they balance perfectly, don't they? Would you then say that both balls, one light and the other many times heavier, moved down the slope in exactly the same time?"

"It would seem so, sir, but Aristotle—"

"For once, Corsi, forget what you have read and use the brain God gave you," Galileo interrupted.

From his seat in front, Professor Santucci grumbled. "You prove nothing about free-falling bodies by racing balls down a slope."

"We do not have the time today," said Galileo, "but try the experiment yourself. Lift the beam higher and higher, each time rolling the balls down the slope. You will find that both balls whether they roll or fall reach the end of the beam together. Despite Aristotle, the speed of a falling body does not depend on its weight.

"And while you are at it you might return to my experiments with the pendulum. Every downward swing of the pendulum, you will admit, is a kind of fall. If Aristotle was right, a heavy weight should swing faster than a light. But try it for yourself. All weights swing in equal times.

"And now, gentlemen, let me ask, you noticed the balls rolling down the slope. Did they gather speed as they moved along? Perhaps our water clock can help us. We know how much time it takes for a ball to roll down our incline. Suppose we rolled it a quarter of the way down. How much time would that take, Corsi?"

"A quarter of the time, sir?"

"Well, let's try," said Galileo. "I'll time the ball and you stop it when it has gone one quarter way down the beam. Let's see. . . . It took half the time it would need to roll the whole distance."

"Then, sir," said Corsi, "if the ball needs one-half the time to go one-quarter the distance, it must be going faster and faster the longer it rolls."

"Good," cried Galileo. "Even Aristotle knew that falling objects gather speed as they fall. I have worked out the formula.

"Suppose our ball is rolling at the end of one second at the rate of five feet per second; at the end of two seconds it will be rolling at a rate of ten feet per second; at the end of three seconds at fifteen feet per second and so on. We can then draw up the following law of motion: the speed of a rolling or falling body varies with the time it takes.

"Now my second law of motion is a law of distance. If a body rolls a certain distance in one second; it will roll four times that distance in two seconds and nine times as far in three seconds and so on. The distance varies with the square of the time, that is, the time multiplied by itself. Therefore, my good Corsi, if a ball rolls three feet the first second, how far should it have gone in two seconds?"

"Two times two, times the distance of three feet or twelve feet, sir."

"And in three seconds?"

"Three times three, times the distance of three feet or twenty-seven feet, sir."

"A worthy pupil," said Galileo, smiling.

"Have you worked out the rate of speed in a free fall?" asked Professor Mazzoni.

"Not yet," said Galileo. "But if we assume that at the end of one second a falling body is moving at the rate of thirty-two feet a second; at the end of two seconds it will be moving at a rate of sixty-four feet a second; at the end of three seconds, at a rate of ninety-six feet a second and so on. In other words the rate will increase thirty-two feet with each second of fall."

Professor Santucci rose out of his seat. "And you are the one who asks us to rely on our eyes and not on books in the search for truth. Who here has ever seen a leaf or feather increasing its speed with each second it falls? Who here, except Professor Galilei, does not know that such light objects hardly seem to fall? Rather they float lazily in the air. If a raindrop fell from a high cloud at the rate you talk about, it would strike a man with the speed of a cannon ball.

And yet even you must be aware that such accidents are rare."

"Excellent! Excellent, Professor Santucci!" cried Galileo, laughing. "But what you say does not contradict my laws of motion. Everything falls through the air. Air like water holds back things moving through it. A leaf or a feather has a very large surface for its size and is therefore held back by the air. On the other hand a streamlined object falls swiftly through the air, just as a fish moves quickly through the water.

"In a vacuum, that is, in the absence of all air, all things, no matter what their shape or size, would fall at the same speed."

"I have never heard such nonsense," Professor Santucci countered. "There can be no such thing as a vacuum. Almighty God Himself could not make a vacuum. Your experiments are without meaning. They do not deal with real things on a real earth. They are only mathematical problems somewhere out in space."

Galileo's class sat in hushed silence as Professor Santucci went on with his attack.

"In your boldness you set yourself up against all the wise men of the past. Aristotle said that objects fall in accord with their weight and no experiment you can ever do will make me change my mind."

Galileo picked up the bronze ball from his desk, played with it a moment and then said sharply, "If that is so, you might just as well put a blindfold about your eyes for the rest of your life. Were Aristotle here today in this classroom, he would be more willing to learn from what he sees than you."

Professor Santucci trembled with anger. "You are impossible," he cried. "I hoped when you returned to Pisa that you had learned some modesty. But no, you haven't changed at all. And now you set yourself up as the teacher of Aristotle. Good day, sir." He rushed out of the room.

As the door slammed the bronze ball fell from Galileo's hand and rolled along the floor.

"Gentlemen," said Galileo, "if you can turn your attention to the ball that slipped from my fingers. Ah, there it has come to a halt against Professor Cesalpino's foot. If I asked why it stopped moving, you'd have a ready answer. Something got in its way. But suppose nothing got in its way, neither the wall, the chairs, the desks, nor a professor's feet. Would it have continued going? And if so, how far? Let us consider these questions at a future meeting."

That evening Jacopo Mazzoni invited Galileo to have dinner with him at a student tavern.

"I would like to celebrate your new science of motion," Jacopo said. "But tell me, what value can these laws of motion have besides annoying our fellow professors?"

Galileo smiled. "Look at this diagram. At the present time the aiming of a cannon is a matter of chance and a good eye. The force of the exploding gunpowder shoots the ball out in a straight line. At the same time the force of gravity is pulling it toward the earth at the rate of speed I worked out for falling bodies. I have discovered that, acted upon by these two forces, the cannon ball takes the curved path we call a parabola. Using my figures, therefore, a cannoneer should be able to score a bull's eye every time he fires."

"Galileo," said Jacopo, "you could be famous for your inventions and your wonderful way of using mathematics to solve scientific problems, that is, if you could stop rubbing the professors the wrong way."

"You're right, Jacopo. I have a temper and whenever I see stupidity I can't help giving it a rap on the head. How can I accept what some greybeard said a thousand years ago when I know that he is just as liable to error as I am? You don't suppose that Santucci ran home to set up an inclined plane or hang a bob from the end of a cord, even just to prove me wrong. Not at all! At this very moment, I'll wager, he's blowing the dust off an ancient book to find another writer who bowed down before Aristotle. I could hit the target a thousand times with a cannon ball and Santucci still would not believe what I said."

"Promise me one thing, Galileo—that next time you will try to control your tongue."

"For your sake, good friend, yes."

"Then enough of this gloom, Galileo. What did you call wine the other day? Wetness mixed with sunlight! Then lift your glass and your voice and join me in song."

Chapter 7 / The Arrow

GALILEO WAS UNHAPPY at Pisa. He was so poorly paid that he was forced to give private lessons and board students in his house. When he was ill he was not paid at all. Once when the Arno overflowed and he could not cross the river, he lost his salary for every day he missed class.

Things were not going well at home. His father was ailing. The family relied on Galileo more and more. To help Virginia get married he had promised to raise the money for her dowry, although he had no idea of where he was going to get it.

What he needed more than anything else was a good position at another university. And for that he would need the help of a powerful friend.

When Galileo received a summons to appear before Giovanni, Governor of the City of Leghorn not far from Pisa, he became quite excited. Giovanni was a Medici, one of the most powerful families in all Italy. Among its members were princes, dukes and popes. No doubt about it, Giovanni's friendship could do a great deal for the young professor.

Giovanni pointed proudly to a model of a dredging machine he himself had designed. He hoped it could be used to clear the harbor of Leghorn. Surely Galileo was going to praise it to the skies. He was a bright young man, clever with his hands, who would appreciate the work of a fellow inventor.

"Well, what do you think?" Giovanni inquired.

Galileo pretended to examine the model carefully although he had seen at his first glance that it was a hopeless muddle.

In his mind he pictured Jacopo Mazzoni shaking his head from side to side: "Flatter Giovanni. Say something pleasant. You can't tell a prince the truth."

But Galileo knew deep within himself that come what may he had to tell the truth as he saw it.

"It won't work!" he said bluntly.

Despite Galileo's warning, Giovanni went ahead and built the machine. He tried it out in Leghorn Harbor and became the laughing stock of Tuscany. His great invention simply refused to work. Instead of blaming himself he swore to even the score with the man who had dared to tell a prince the truth.

He did not wait long. One day soon after, Galileo entered his class and found a number of strangers seated in the rear. His students, generally quite noisy before the lecture began, were unusually quiet. Galileo strode to the platform.

"On the desk," he said, "you will see an ordinary fly-wheel which has been most carefully oiled. If Signore Corsi will kindly set the wheel in motion—thank you. Now, gentlemen, if you can take your eyes off the wheel, you will recall that not so long ago I suggested a problem to you: what would happen to a rolling ball if nothing whatever got in its way?

"It is our aim, today, to try to solve that problem. Again we begin with Aristotle. According to him, natural motion is the movement of an object toward the earth. The fall of an apple from a tree, for example, is natural motion. Sideways motion, let us say, the flight of an arrow, he calls violent or unnatural motion. It is contrary to what it wants to do, which is to fall to the earth and rest. The things in this world, Aristotle seems to think, are like a lazy man sitting in the sun who is not going to move unless he is forced to."

"Three cheers for Aristotle," a voice from the rear suddenly shouted. Some of the students turned around and cried, "Quiet." But Galileo went on as though he had not heard.

"All of this seems to make good common sense. The flywheel did not spin around until our friend Corsi poked it. A bullet does not shoot out of the gun until the gunpowder explodes. An arrow does not go forward until I release the bowstring.

"But then why should an arrow after it has left the bow keep on moving forward? Should it not, the moment it loses contact with the bowstring, fall to the ground and lie at rest?

"Aristotle's followers explain the continuing movement of the arrow by saying that the air itself does the moving."

From this point on, the back benches broke into cheers and applause every time Galileo mentioned Aristotle's name.

"As the arrow moves forward, they say, it squeezes the air in front which then rushes behind the arrow and pushes it along. The air takes up the job of moving the arrow where the bowstring left off. That no one has ever noticed the air behaving in this odd manner does not bother the followers of Aristotle. They insist that nothing can continue to move unless there is something to keep it on the move. But then, what keeps the moon, the planets and the other heavenly bodies moving? They answer this question by saying that a series of hollow balls or spheres surround our earth. As they turn they carry the heavenly bodies along with them. Unfortunately for those who thought up this scheme, astronomy has shown that such spheres do not exist at all. We have to look elsewhere for an explanation of what keeps the heavens moving."

Now it was the turn of Galileo's students to applaud while those in the back hissed and booed.

"Let us, like good scientists," said Galileo, still paying no attention to the noise in the room, "take a close look at the idea that the air moves objects forward. If that is so, why should they ever stop? And yet we know that arrows, like stones and cannon balls, finally do stop moving.

"In the second place how could an object ever fly against the wind when it is the air that is supposed to be pushing it forward? In the third place we should be able to test whether in fact the air pushes an object ahead. Let us tie a long ribbon to the end of an arrow. If the idea is correct, the ribbon should blow ahead of the arrow. But alas, who here today will insist that he has ever seen a ribbon acting in such a manner?"

In the rear voices started to chant: "Wrangler! Wrangler!"

"It should be perfectly clear to all now," continued Galileo calmly, "that the idea is not valid, no matter how famous those who believe in it. But then you ask: *What does keep objects moving?*

"Up to the present time we have thought that it was natural for a thing to be at rest. To keep it moving some unseen hand such as the air had to go along with it and prod it on. Let us, however, look at the problem from another angle. Let us say, instead, that it is natural for an object to be in movement.

"For example, I roll this ball along my desk. When I put my hand in the way it stops. Are we right in saying that the ball will keep moving until something gets in its path? That something may be my hand, the rough wood of the desk, the inkstand, anything at all. But something must be in the way before the ball will stop. We all know that the smoother we make the path, the farther the ball will roll. Could we build a perfectly smooth path, the ball

would roll out of the room, out of Pisa and around the world.

"But one of my bright pupils asks, 'What of the resistance of the air?' I answer, 'Let the air be removed and the ball will continue forever in a state of motion.'

"With these observations in mind I have drawn up a law which simply states that objects in a state of rest will remain in a state of rest and objects in movement will continue to maintain that movement, until acted upon by another force."

The entire hall was now a riot of noise and disorder. The strangers were openly jeering while the students raised their fists and cried, "Shame." Corsi had rushed to the rear to quiet the uproar and was struggling with one of the visitors. Two of his friends were attempting to separate them. Galileo's last words went unheard even by those in the front row.

"Can this law explain the movement of the heavenly bodies? I believe it can. It does away with the invisible spheres and every other kind of sky machinery. The moon, the planets, the comets and the stars are in movement because there is no other force to stop them. We may therefore expect them to keep in movement forever. Our law then explains movement not only on earth but also in the heavens.

"And now if we may turn back to the flywheel on my desk, which is now taking its last slow spin around. To sum up our lesson will one of you please tell the class why it kept moving and why it has now stopped? Corsi, what about you? Ah, I see that our good friend is busy with other matters.

"Gentlemen," Galileo concluded with a grim smile, looking over the shouting, struggling room, "I can only hope that this lecture has been of some profit to you."

Giovanni's campaign to drive Galileo out of the university made rapid progress. He spoke to the professors who already had no great love for Galileo and they in turn passed the word on to their students.

Obstinate and proud, Galileo was never one to help his own cause. In a discussion he had a way of appearing to they had not thought of. Then, when they seemed on the agree with his opponents and even fed them arguments very edge of victory, he would destroy their position with one deadly, inescapable argument or demonstration. It was a method which amused Galileo's friends but enraged his ever-growing circle of enemies.

Many people were especially aroused against Galileo because he was turning his scientific investigations toward the heavens. According to the ancient scholars, heaven and earth were completely separate. The heavens were the dwelling place of spirits and angels and the home of Almighty God. Unlike the substance of the earth, the material of the stars and planets was perfect, never changing or decaying.

According to Galileo, however, heaven and earth were not so different. The very laws that governed the movement of such ordinary earthly things as rolling balls also directed the movement of the glorious heavenly bodies. "In fact," Galileo seemed to be saying, "the entire universe is controlled by uniform physical laws."

The professors could not accept this challenge to all they believed without fighting back. Life at the university became more and more difficult for Galileo. He was greeted with jeers and hisses wherever he went; after a while even his most loyal students began to drop away.

Galileo was stubborn. He probably would have stayed on at Pisa no matter how he was treated. But news now came that his father was dead and as the eldest son he became the breadwinner of the family. His salary was not enough for his mother, two sisters, brother and himself.

Virginia was married at last and her husband kept demanding the dowry Galileo had foolishly promised. His brother Michelangelo was a talented musician, but vain and lazy.

"Why can't he get a part-time job and help out at home?" Galileo asked.

"Poor child," Giulia replied. "Do you want to take his rest and fun away from him?"

Those who knew Galileo only as a tough, harsh foe would have been surprised to see how tender-hearted he could be. Often he did not have enough for a decent meal. Yet he managed to save a few pennies to send gifts home.

"I'm bringing a set of silken bed curtains for Virginia," he wrote to his mother. "There is enough silk left over for a cover for your bed. But keep it all a secret because I want to surprise her when I come."

In 1591 after three years of teaching, Galileo gave up his job and went home to Florence to be the head of the household. Before he left Pisa, he met Professor Cesalpino in the shadow of the Leaning Tower.

"You seem to have won after all," Galileo said.

"It would have been different, had you taken my advice, Professor Galilei. But perhaps you will be ready to listen to me when you are older and wiser."

Galileo looked at him skeptically. "I don't think I ever will," he said.

Chapter 8 / Death at the Stake

In 1592 GALILEO won a professorship in mathematics at the University of Padua in northern Italy with a salary almost three times higher than the one he had received at Pisa.

Padua was one of the oldest schools in Europe. From its very beginning the teachers were a tough, independent lot who insisted on the freedom to teach as they saw fit. In 1222 the teachers at the University of Bologna had become unhappy with the way they were treated. One morning the professors took off their long black robes, padlocked their classrooms and went on strike. When their demands were refused, they rallied their students, marched out of town in a body and started their own school in the city of Padua, not far from Venice.

Padua soon became well-known. Its great libraries, famous teachers and medical school brought students from all over Europe. William Harvey, the discoverer of the circulation of the blood, came from England to study there. Kings and princes sent their children, who brought along with them their own special teachers, clerks and servants. A few students came not to study but to have a good time and sometimes sent their servants to take their places in class.

Padua was under the rule of Venice, the great north Italian city built on a series of islands that jutted out into the Adriatic Sea. In 1571 at the battle of Lepanto the Turkish fleet had been destroyed by the Venetian navy. Venetian ships ranged the Mediterranean and the Far East bringing great wealth and power to the "Queen of the Adriatic."

Venice was one of the few states in Europe that was a republic. Its ruler, called the Doge, did not inherit his title but was elected to his high office by two law-making bodies, the Senate and the Council of Ten.

One of Galileo's best friends was the nobleman Giovanni Sagredo, a member of the powerful Council of Ten. Giovanni loved science and Galileo often came to Venice to see him. His home was a kind of Noah's Ark in which he kept all sorts of strange animals.

Like Giovanni, Galileo was a man of many interests. Busy as he was at the university, he still managed to find time for his inventions. One of his most popular instruments, the military compass, brought in so many orders that he had to open a workshop in his own home. To help him with the work he hired a master mechanic, Marcantonio Mazzoleni, who moved into the house with his wife and children.

The military compass was made of two straight rulers hinged at one end so that they could be set at any angle. It was useful for solving mathematical problems and enlarging charts and maps.

In all his life, Galileo once said, he never knew an idle moment. He enjoyed spending time in his workshop, making things of his own invention, trying out new experiments and training his assistants. Using his hands was second nature to him. The craftsmanship of the master artisan was combined in him with the genius of the scientist. Galileo had a way of observing levers, balances, gears and machines so that he knew them from the inside out, the way a good doctor knows the human body.

Although his inventions did very well, Galileo still was short of money. In addition to helping his mother, brother and sisters, he now had to support a family of his own. In 1598 Galileo had met and fallen in love with a beautiful young woman from Venice named Marina Gamba. Their first daughter, Virginia, was born in 1600.

Besides his own family and the Mazzolenis, Galileo sometimes had as many as twenty students living in his house, some with their own servants. In fact, he was running a kind of combined private school and factory, at the same time teaching at the university.

Galileo's life in Padua settled into an untroubled routine. After a hard day's work he would often serve supper in the garden under the trees he himself had planted. He would exchange ideas with his friends and students and perhaps show them an invention on which he was working. Girolamo Fabrici, a doctor famous throughout Europe, and Benedetto Castelli, who would become a leader of Italian science, were frequent guests of Galileo.

One early summer evening Galileo sat in the garden with Fabrici and Castelli. He surveyed the peaceful scene with pleasure. On his right stood the Church of San Giustino and on his left the large and comfortable house he had recently bought. At the far end of the garden a student was playing the lute while others read or walked about, talking quietly.

"How my life has changed since I came here to Padua eight years ago," Galileo thought. "I have good friends and admiring students. I can speak my mind and say what I believe. Not at all bad for a professor who once faced empty classrooms and was hooted and hissed as he walked through the streets!"

Galileo turned to his two friends. "Wonders are all about us," he said, "if we only have eyes to see them. Look at this small glass bottle. Nothing unusual about it except for the long straw-like neck! But see what happens when I cup the bottle in my hands for a few moments, turn it upside down and slip the neck into this saucer of water. There! I've removed my hand from the bottle and the water rises halfway up the neck. My good friends, can you tell me why?"

Galileo looked into their puzzled eyes. "Well," he repeated, "why did the water rise?"

"Let's see," Castelli said slowly. "You held the bottle in your hands, you dipped the neck into the saucer of water, the water rose into the tube. I'm sure your holding the bottle in your hands for a while had something to do with it. But what, I don't know."

Dr. Fabrici said, "I know the explanation is quite simple. All of Galileo's explanations are quite simple, once you know them. I suppose it is as plain as the nose on my face."

"Even plainer," Galileo replied, "as plain as the air about you. Look, my friends. I wrap my hands over the bottle. What have I done? That's it, I've warmed the air inside. The heated air expands and some is forced out. When I put the neck into the saucer, the water rises to take the place of the air."

"A very neat trick," said Castelli, "but what on earth do you do with it?"

"Look carefully, my practical Benedetto," said Galileo. "I bring a candle close to the bottle."

"The water level is sinking," cried Castelli.

"Exactly! The flame warms whatever air is left in the bottle. The air expands and forces the water level down. Now I remove the candle, the air cools and shrinks and—"

"The water level rises," said Fabrici. "Now I see what you are up to. You have invented a device men have long sought, a way of taking temperature. Place it outside your

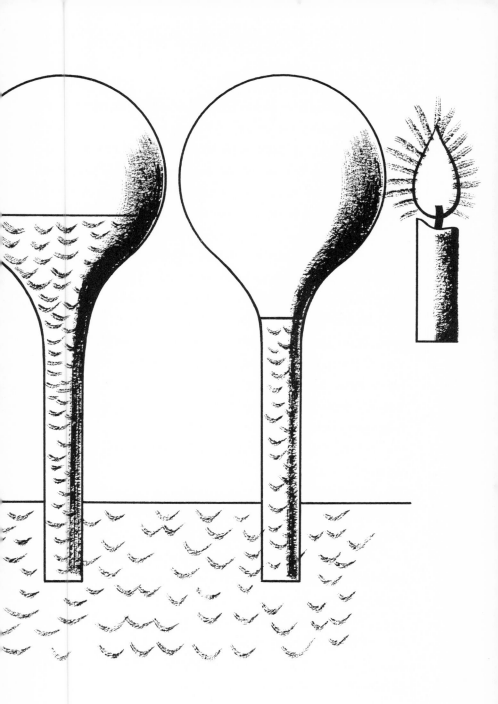

window and you will be able to measure the heat and cold of the day."

"But you will need some sort of scale to tell you just how hot or cold it is," Castelli pointed out. "Divide the neck of the bottle into one hundred units and any child can then read off the temperature."

"A good idea. A few more like that and, who knows, I may take you into business with—But look who's here!" Galileo cried, starting up from the table.

Through the garden gate came Giulia, Livia and Michelangelo.

Giulia hugged her son. "How richly dressed you are!"

With advancing years Giulia had gained weight but her tongue was as sharp as ever. "How little you must care for your poor relatives in Florence. We never hear from you these days. 'Your son,' someone said, 'is one of the richest men in Padua, and is seen only with the nobility.'"

"Mother, allow me to present my good friends to you, Dr. Fabrici, who teaches at Padua's medical school, and my brightest pupil, Benedetto Castelli."

"Ah, gentlemen," said Giulia, "you'd never think he had a mother for all the attention he pays me. I have never even seen this fine house."

"Well, then, let me show it to you at once," Galileo hurried his mother indoors.

"Michel, my love," Giulia urged, "tell Galileo your good news. What are you waiting for?"

"Galileo, my dear brother," Michelangelo cried, "I've become music master for a noble family, one of the greatest in all Europe. I have two servants to wait on me, a coach with four white horses and a princely salary. You should be proud of your brother."

"Very proud," Giulia echoed.

Galileo said nothing. His brother was certain to have a hidden motive.

"Galileo would never stand in my way," Michelangelo went on. "Isn't that what I said to you, Mother?"

"Your very words," Giulia nodded.

"To put the matter plainly, Galileo, the job is in Poland. What I need are travel expenses, musical instruments and some good clothing. These rags are all I have in the world."

Giulia added, "My Galileo would never want his brother to look like a beggar."

"Mother," said Galileo, "I've sent you money regularly for the last eight years. I can't afford to give you more. Don't forget that I also have a family of my own."

"Don't tell your old mother you haven't lots of money. I've heard all about the sons of the nobility who board here with you."

"I charge my students only enough to cover household costs," Galileo explained. "I'm not a businessman, Mother."

"You are right," said Giulia bitterly. "You were never one to think of earning a penny, but you let your poor parents work for you and never showed any thanks."

"When Father died," said Galileo, "I took his place as head of the family and I have taken care of you ever since. You forget I gave the dowry for Virginia's marriage."

"Yes," said Michelangelo, "but not before her husband said he'd throw you into jail if you ever set foot in Florence."

"Enough of the past," Giulia intervened. "What are you going to do for your poor sister Livia? It's impossible to live with her; all day long she moans. Her dear brother has forgotten her. Why doesn't he send her silk for a new dress? How is she to get a husband if she cannot be seen out of doors?

"I say to her, 'Your brother's not a rich man.' You see I am on your side, Galileo. 'Enter a convent,' I say, 'for all your brother cares. Our professor has more on his mind than getting you a husband.' "

"I have news for her," Galileo said. "She can stop worrying about entering a convent. I've made a match for her with a very fine young man, Taddeo Galletti of Pisa. The only trouble is that I've promised a dowry of 1,800 ducats, 800 to be paid at once and the rest over a five-year period."

"Are you mad?" cried Giulia, pleased at getting her last daughter married off, but frightened at the thought of raising such a huge sum. "Where will you get so much money?"

"I can borrow 800, that is, if Michel will promise to repay half just as soon as he is working. In return I will fit him out with whatever he needs."

Michelangelo kissed his brother, "Galileo, sleep soundly. Remember that if there is anyone in this wide world on whom you can depend, it is I, your brother."

"Then it is all settled," said Galileo. "Let us go and give the news to my good friends."

In the garden he called out, "Dear friends, this is one of the happiest days of my life. Here I am in my own home surrounded by my loving family, my first-born child just a month old and my dear sister—"

Castelli walked up to Galileo and whispered, "Brother Sarpi is at the door and wishes to see you."

"Ask him in, ask him in," cried Galileo. "I am about to announce the marriage of my sister Livia."

"But he would rather see you alone."

Paolo Sarpi, a Servite monk, was one of the most powerful men in Venice, a close friend and adviser to the Doge and a fearless and free mind. He knew everything of importance that went on in Italy.

Galileo rushed to the door to greet his friend. "Paolo, it is good to see you. But why so serious?"

In the garden the music of the lute had stopped. The last light from the west was gone, the air had grown chill.

"The news I bring is not of a happy nature," Paolo whispered. "I have just received word from Rome that Giordano Bruno was burned at the stake!"

Chapter 9 / The Right to Speak

LONG AFTER HIS mother, brother and sister had gone to bed and far into the night, Galileo talked to his friends about the death of Giordano Bruno.

"For eight years they kept him in prison all by himself," said Brother Sarpi. "Then they led him into a public square and set the flames under him. All Rome was there, a fine beginning for the new century. I doubt that we have heard the end of it."

"Did they torture him?" asked Castelli.

"Again and again," Sarpi said. "But they could not break his spirit. Up to the end he refused to say he was wrong."

"You have to agree he had some very strange ideas," remarked Dr. Fabrici.

"In Venice, unlike Rome," Sarpi said, "we do not harm a man for his ideas."

"How foolish he was," said Castelli. "Living in France

he was as safe as he would have been here. But once he dared return to his homeland they had him. Why did they do it? Why?"

"One of my agents reports," said Sarpi, "that as the fire was lighted, he turned to his judges and said, 'You who judge me, perhaps you are in greater fear than I whom you have judged.'"

Galileo spoke at last. "A brave man," he said. "I wonder what I would have done in his place."

Dr. Fabrici looked at Galileo in amazement. "But surely you don't believe in ideas like his!"

The others turned and waited for Galileo to answer.

The Italian priest Giordano Bruno had said some very strange things: that, for example, the earth was not the center of the world; that the sun was not the only sun in the universe but one of many about which other earths circled; that on those far-off planets beings like men offered their prayers to Almighty God also.

How dared Bruno tamper with the plan of the universe? Did he not know that the world was a closed hollow ball in which, one within the other, were eighty glassy spheres holding the stars, the sun, the planets, the seven planets and the moon? The spheres turned forever about the earth which hung firm and motionless in the very center of the universe.

Such a plan had been approved by Aristotle, then by the learned geographer and astronomer of the second century A.D. Ptolemy, and later by the Church.

Who could doubt it, especially when it made good sense? Look at the sun. Did it not move through the sky, rising in the east, swinging across the heavens, and going down in the west? And the next morning was it not in the east ready to start its journey all over again? Did that not prove that it went around the earth?

All this talk of Bruno's, about the earth moving through the sky as though it were just a moon or planet, was nonsense. No one had ever seen the earth move.

It was true that a half century before, Nicolaus Copernicus, an official of the Cathedral of Frauenberg in Poland, had had a similar idea. He thought the earth had not one but two motions, both, mind you, at the same time.

"Not only," said he, "does the earth swing in a great circle once a year about the sun but it also, like a spinning top, turns on itself every twenty-four hours, showing first one side to the sun and then the other."

When you thought about it, the idea wasn't entirely mad for it gave an explanation of the cause of day and night.

But people weren't going to be fooled by such thinking. They said, "If the earth is spinning around so fast, why don't we go sliding off? Why doesn't a big wind come up that sweeps birds out of their nests and tumbles high buildings? Perhaps, Copernicus, you feel such a wind. We don't!"

People laughed so much that Copernicus did not dare publish his book until he was on his deathbed. And by that time the world had forgotten all about him and his strange ideas.

No, you could not take that Polish madman seriously But what about Tycho Brahe, the Danish astronomer. No one in the Church or in the universities could question his work on the heavens. He was the most careful and pain-staking stargazer that ever lived. In his great observatory, Uraniborg, which the King of Denmark had built for him, he studied the stars night after night after night and year after year. He knew them the way a father knows his own children.

He was never happy with one or two or even three observations of a planet but followed its complete path through the sky. And he wasn't one to be taken in by the Copernican hocus-pocus about the earth's going around the sun either. If a motionless earth was good enough for Aris-totle and Ptolemy, it was good enough for Tycho Brahe.

But in 1577 he got a shock that forced him to change a few of his ideas. It was the year a great comet passed through the heavens. Tycho worked out its path. To his sur-prise it was going beyond the sun. But to do that, it would have to go through the sphere of the moon and the spheres of each of the planets.

How could a comet slip through not one but nine hard spheres each solid enough to carry a heavenly body? Tycho saw only one answer. The spheres did not exist at all.

But Tycho's discovery did not mean that Aristotle and

Ptolemy were wrong about the earth and the sun. The earth was still at the center of the universe and the sun still circled about it.

Nor could there be any doubt for it was in the Bible. Did not Joshua, when he besieged Jericho, cry, "Sun, stand thou still; stand thou still." Surely Joshua would not have told the sun to stand still if it was still already. Instead he would have said, "Earth, stand thou still, stand thou still." The Bible then was the final proof that it was the sun and not the earth that moved.

For more than one thousand years the Church, headed by the Pope in Rome, had reigned supreme in Europe. But in 1517 Martin Luther, a German monk, challenged the religious authority of Rome and laid the foundation for the Protestant faith. While Italy, Spain, France and parts of central Europe remained faithful to the Roman Catholic Church, most of the countries of northern Europe, including Holland and England, broke away. Troubled by the Protestant revolt, the Church became very sensitive to any disagreement about religious beliefs.

A Church court called the Inquisition had been set up long ago to stamp out heresy. In the late sixteenth century the judges or Inquisitors earnestly took up the task of locating heretics, those who held incorrect religious ideas, and of helping them to see the error of their ways. Men like Giordano Bruno who stubbornly refused to admit they were wrong were imprisoned and sometimes tortured and put to death.

"We are not cruel men," the judges said. "It is far better to suffer on earth than to be punished forever in the world after death."

When the inquisitors came to a city, no man felt safe. A neighbor might have reported him to the court. A man might be completely without guilt but the mere sight of the torture instruments was enough to loosen his tongue. Before he knew it, he would be admitting to the worst crimes.

One inquisitor, Nicolas Remy of Lorraine, put to death over nine hundred men, women and children. Almost all of them, before they died, admitted they were witches!

Men feared the dreaded knock on the door in the early morning hours and the order to appear at the court. Kings and princes did the Inquisition's bidding. In all of Italy the only state that refused to obey the Holy Office, as it was called, was the Republic of Venice.

Galileo himself had been affected by the climate of his times. He had thought about the ideas of Copernicus for many years. Gradually he had come to believe that they were true. Yet in his classes at Padua he was still teaching the old views of Aristotle and Ptolemy.

What was he now to say to his friends?

At last he declared, "I will share my secret with you. I am a follower of Copernicus. But I dare not tell the world, lest like my master I should be laughed at or like Bruno be executed."

"Do not fear," said Castelli. "Your secret is safe with us."

"There is yet another reason I do not speak," said Galileo. "Suppose one of you were to say to me, 'Galileo, tell me truly, do you know *as a fact* that the earth goes about the sun?' I would have to answer you, 'At the present time I have no real proof. All I can say is that it seems more reasonable to believe that the earth goes about the sun than that the sun moves about the earth.' "

"Reasonable!" cried Dr. Fabrici. "But don't our eyes show us the sun, stars and planets moving over the sky?"

"Our senses may trick us," Galileo said, "into believing that the heavens are moving. We are on an earth that is turning round and round and this gives us the idea that the heavens are swinging around us."

"I see what you mean," said Castelli. "My back is turned to the Church of San Guistino at the end of your garden. In order to see it shall I demand that the whole landscape turn around me or shall I just turn my head around? It is more reasonable to suppose that the earth, like my body, turns than to suppose that the entire universe turns around the earth. But if the earth is moving," he went on, "why don't we feel the movement? If we drop a stone from a tower, shouldn't it land some distance away? If we shoot an arrow against the direction of the earth's movement should it not fall behind us?"

"The moving earth," said Galileo, "carries everything along with it. It is very much like being on a smoothly sailing ship. The ship moves quietly over the ocean as the earth through space. Passengers and crew move about freely and go about their business just as though the ship were in harbor. Indeed if he did not leave his cabin a passenger might not know the ship was moving. So it is with those who dwell on this great ship, the earth."

"Let us return," said Castelli, "to the earth's movement about the sun. Doesn't the earth have to travel great distances in the course of the year to get around the sun. If that is so, why don't the stars look different to us? As a traveler gets closer to distant mountains they begin to look different. Yet the stars look exactly the same no matter how far the earth travels."

"A good question," Galileo said. "My guess is that the stars are so far away we will never see the change."

"Then the heavens must indeed be vast," said Dr. Fabrici. "What good is so much empty space to man?"

"Well, Benedetto," said Galileo, "what do you say?"

Castelli thought for a moment. "That I do not know the use of something does not mean it isn't there. Jupiter exists whether or not it does me any good. Then for all we know space may not be as empty as we think. Some day new planets and stars may be discovered."

Sarpi began to laugh. "Enough," he cried. "New planets, new stars! Aristotle or Copernicus! Sun about the earth or earth about the sun! My head begins to ache with all your talk. All I know is that a man has the right to be for or against any one of these ideas if he so chooses. Unless there is freedom how are we ever to find what is right and what is wrong? When the time is ripe, Galileo, do not fear to speak out. The Republic of Venice will protect you."

Chapter 10 / The Turning Point

IN THE FALL of 1604 something happened in the skies that was to change the whole course of Galileo's life.

On October 9th of that year a new star appeared near the Constellation of the Serpent. Sparkling with ever-changing color—tawny, yellow, purple, red and white—it almost outshone Venus, the brightest planet in the sky.

What did it mean?

Many remembered the Star of 1572 which had burst into the heavens just before the Massacre of St. Bartholomew's Day when thousands of people in France were killed in bloody conflict between Catholics and Protestants.

What would happen now—earthquakes? plagues? famines? Who could tell? Did not the stars have a great influence on mankind? Mars was known to cause terrible wars and Venus helped lovers.

One's future could be read in the stars. A wise general did not go forth to battle, a merchant complete a sale or a traveler set out for a distant city unless the stars were right.

How was one to find out? By calling on the nearest astrologer or star-reader. After glancing at the stars and pocketing his fee, he let one know what was in store. If he was right, one told one's friends about him. If he was wrong, one went elsewhere the next time. Only a very foolhardy man would neglect to see his astrologer at important moments in his life.

The Italian mathematician and astrologer, Jerome Cardan, once foretold his own death. But unfortunately, when the time came for him to die, he was still very much alive. There was nothing left for him to do but to starve himself to death. Most astrologers, however, did not go that far.

Great scientists sometimes were forced to practice astrology. In order to earn a living Johannes Kepler had to pretend he could see the future in the stars. On the other hand, his master Tycho Brahe passionately believed in astrology.

When Galileo became mathematician to the Grand Duke of Tuscany, he was asked by the Grand Duchess Cristina to read her husband's horoscope or future.

"I know you are the world's greatest astrologer," she insisted.

Galileo growled. "Astronomer, Madame, not astrologer. An astrologer is a fortuneteller. I am an astronomer, a scientist who studies the stars."

"Astronomer or astrologer, you must at once draw up my dear husband's horoscope."

Galileo was right. He was no astrologer. He foretold that the Duchess' husband would live to a ripe old age. Three weeks later the Duke was dead.

Watched closely by astronomers, astrologers and ordinary people, the new star of 1604 shone bright and then like the Star of 1572 began to fade. After eighteen months it was gone, together with all the terrible things the seers had said about it.

While it still shone clearly in the heavens, Galileo announced that he would give a number of talks about it. At the opening talk over a thousand students and professors jammed the Magna Aula or Great Hall of the University of Padua. Hundreds who could not get in crowded the halls, lobbies and even the street outside, hoping to hear a few words about the new star.

"Why are you so excited about this star?" Galileo asked calmly. "Nothing unusual is going to happen. The coming of this star is a natural event, not a supernatural one. To understand it we must make use of the methods of science, astronomy and mathematics.

"Why do you marvel so much about it? Every day of our lives we can see marvels of nature. What can be as wonderful as the daily rising of the sun? Yet if I gave a talk on the rising of the sun I could not fill the front row of this hall. Do we lack feeling for God's wonders just because they happen more than once?"

The talk went along quietly until Professor Cesare Cremonino got up to ask a question. Although he strongly believed in Aristotle, he liked and respected Galileo. At Padua, unlike Pisa, a man could disagree with you sharply and still remain your friend.

"Professor Galilei, in your opinion is this new body a star or a comet?"

"Without a doubt, a star," said Galileo.

A murmur arose in the hall. How can Professor Galilei call it a star? When God created the universe did He not create it perfectly with just the right number of stars? The professor was going too far.

"Then what you are saying," said Professor Cremonino, "is that the universe is not perfect. And yet all you have to do is to look up into the heavens to see how perfect it is. Look at the perfect roundness of the sun. See how perfectly smooth is the surface of the moon. Notice the exact circle the sun and the planets make as they go about our earth. Nothing is out of place or crooked. All follow a most excellent order and balance."

"What you say is very beautiful," Galileo replied, "but it is not science. How do you know the sun is perfectly round, the surface of the moon perfectly smooth, the path of the sun about the earth a perfect circle? How do you know that the sun goes about the earth?

"I ask for proof and you give me pretty words. You remind me of a man who once wanted to sell me an invention by which I could talk to others two and even three thousand miles away. I told him that I'd be most happy to buy it no matter how high the price if he would only give me proof that it worked. It would be quite enough for me, I said, if I placed myself in one corner of the room and he in the other. He then said that over such a short distance his invention would hardly work at all. I responded that it wasn't convenient for me just then to travel to Russia or Egypt to try out his experiment. But if he chose to go there I'd remain in Padua and take part in it. I never heard from him again."

Professor Cremonino joined in the roar of laughter that followed and then said, "Tell me, Professor Galilei, are you a follower of Nicolaus Copernicus?"

A hush fell over the great crowd. Everyone strained to hear what Galileo was about to say.

Galileo looked over the hall. In one of the front rows sat Benedetto Castelli and Giovanni Sagredo, Galileo's protector and adviser. Giovanni half held up his hand. He seemed to be saying, "Careful! Be careful!"

For a moment Castelli, Sagredo and the great silent hall faded away. A boy and his father stood before Michelangelo's statue of David in the great square of Florence, the star of 1572 above their heads. They had just come from fishing in the Arno River. What had the boy's father said about David?

> *All by himself he stood up*
> *for what he knew was right!*

Galileo turned to his audience. "I am a Copernican," he said firmly.

For Galileo there was now no going back. For good or ill his life was tied to the new astronomy. He became the chief champion of Copernicus and openly taught and wrote that the earth moved around the sun. All Europe split into two camps, on one side the great majority of churchmen and professors who fought Galileo bitterly and on the other side the small brave group of friends and scientists who defended him.

Galileo had asked Professor Cremonino for proof that Aristotle and Ptolemy were right. Cremonino had none to offer, but then neither did Galileo. How could anyone tell what the stars and planets were really like? They were so far away. If only there were some way of bringing them close up. Such a chance came to Galileo in 1609.

A visitor just returned from Holland brought some rather odd news. "Have you heard about a Dutchman called Hans Lippershey, who makes eyeglasses in the town of Middelburg? A few months back he was squinting through a lens and suddenly the church steeple, a mile down the road, had slid right next door to him. The sexton was pulling at the bell rope as though he were outside the window and yet you could hardly hear the bell.

"Lippershey then noticed that he had been looking at the church tower not only through the lens in his hand but also through a second one that happened to be resting on the window ledge. He put the two lenses in a tube and now he goes around saying he can see things far off as though they were close by anytime he wants to. Sounds like witchcraft to me. What do you think?"

Galileo could hardly get rid of his visitor fast enough. Minutes later he was digging into a box where he kept odd pieces of glass.

"If this report is true—but let me check before I get excited about it. Let's take a peek through these two pieces. Hm, makes absolutely no difference."

Galileo began humming to himself:

> *Oh, Hans Lippershey, Hans Lippershey,*
> *I can't believe a word you say.*

"But what have we here?"

Galileo had picked out a piece of convex glass, a piece thicker in the middle than at the edges.

"A convex lens enlarges things nicely, but it also blurs them. What I need now is a—"

He took up a concave lens, a piece thinner in the middle than at the edges. Then he fitted both pieces into a lead tube and looked out the window. What he saw made him sing out in a loud voice:

> *Oh, Hans Lippershey, Hans Lippershey,*
> *I'll thank you for many a day!*

Galileo had made his first telescope. Things seen through it seemed three times closer and nine times larger than when seen with the naked eye. His second telescope enlarged objects sixty times their size. Still not satisfied, Galileo worked all his spare time, grinding his lenses with great care and exactness. At last he had an instrument that enlarged things one thousand times and brought them thirty times closer than if seen without its help.

The entire town was soon buzzing with talk of Professor Galilei's spyglass. All day long a steady stream of friends and students trooped through his house to look through the "gun." In August, Antonio Priuli, one of the governors of the university, appeared, dressed in all his robes of office.

"I have the honor to tell you," he said "that news of your new invention has reached the ears of his Highness, the Doge. He asks the immediate pleasure of your presence at the Ducal Palace and requests you to bring your latest spyglass."

In Venice the Doge's own gondola waited for Professor Galilei. In a few moments the entire party was gliding along the Grand Canal. Venice was the most beautiful city in Europe. Crowded close together, houses and gardens seemed to float on the dark green waters of the canals. Churches and palaces gleamed with mosaics of gold.

The Doge's gondola swept under the Rialto, the great bridge that holds shops and markets, and tied up at a mooring post painted like a peppermint stick. Galileo stood in the Piazza di San Marco, Saint Mark's Square, the very heart of the great island city. To his left was the Campanile or Bell Tower, the tallest building in Venice. On his right was St. Mark's Church, with its statues of great horses and glittering murals, and the Doge's Palace.

At the doors of the palace a great company awaited Galileo—senators and noblemen with flowing beards, wearing bright colored togas and pill-box hats. With the Doge and the Dogess in the lead the entire company marched across the square. A huge flock of pigeons rose in flight and whirred over their heads.

The entire group then climbed to the top of the Bell Tower where Galileo handed his spyglass to the Doge. Two inches wide and two feet long it was made of sheet metal and covered with a crimson cloth.

The Doge pointed the "gun" towards the sea. "I think I can make out a great ship far out at sea. I see it clearly now, one of our own vessels returning from China."

"I see nothing at all," cried the Dogess. "Here, let me look."

Rapidly the telescope was passed from hand to hand. Everyone gazed and everyone marveled.

Sagredo exclaimed, "Galileo, I can see the Church of San Guistino next door to your house in Padua. It looks as though it is on the other side of the Grand Canal. Yet I swear it must be twenty-five miles off."

One noble lady peered for a long time and then said, "There will be no secrets left in Venice unless people learn to close their shutters."

Finally the Doge spoke and all were silent. "You have done the Venetian state a great service, Professor Galilei. With this spyglass no enemy will ever be able to surprise us. We will see them long before they see us. What say you?"

"It can be of great help in warfare," Galileo agreed. But he was already thinking of far different uses for his invention.

A few days later Galileo appeared at the Ducal Palace and presented one of his telescopes to the Doge. Antonio Priuli unfurled a long scroll and read:

Be it known to all present this 25th day of August in the year of Our Lord 1609, Master Galileo Galilei, having been professor of mathematics in the University of Padua for seventeen years, and having given to the world certain discoveries and inventions such as the thermometer and the military compass and especially having invented an instrument by which far off things are brought close:

The Council of the Republic of Venice does hereby make him professor for the rest of his life and gives him a salary of one thousand florin a year.

The company broke into loud applause and Galileo's friends cheered.

Galileo's salary had been more than tripled. He was sure of a lifetime position free of all money worries. He need fear neither poverty, the followers of Aristotle nor the Inquisition.

Chapter 11 / Pioneer of Space

To SEE THINGS far off as though they were near!

Galileo now had an instrument by which he could master the vastness of space. It did not matter to him that his spyglass could be useful for armies and navies. He had only one question: could it bring the heavens close to him?

He built a telescope eleven times as powerful as the one he had given the Doge. On the first clear night he turned it toward the skies. At once the doors of heaven slid open and Galileo beheld sights never before seen by man.

The world above him was filled with new things. The Milky Way was no longer a mysterious glow in the night sky but a vast crowd of stars grouped in clusters.

Galileo was exultant. "Wherever I look, thousands of new stars swim into view. Many are large and quite bright while the smaller ones are without number. Men have counted nine stars in the Constellation of Orion. I see not nine but over five hundred. The six we have always seen in the Pleiades are suddenly increased to forty-six. In whatever direction I turn, the universe grows larger and larger. How grand is the real world from the toy model invented by Aristotle and Ptolemy!"

Discovery followed discovery during the month of January, 1610. Sleep was out of the question. Galileo was at his telescope every clear night, sometimes in the company of Sagredo, most often alone. For thousands of years men had looked up at the stars and had made up stories about them. Galileo was the first to see them clearly. "I am quite beside myself with wonder," he said. "I give thanks to God who has allowed me to discover such marvels!"

Galileo turned his telescope toward the moon. It was not perfectly round as the professors had claimed. Nor did it have the smooth surface we see when we look at it with our unaided eyes. Instead, it was pitted and wrinkled with ridges, craters and mountains, some of them higher than those on earth. The surface of the moon was as rough as the one on which we live.

He noticed that when the mountains of the moon on the side facing the sun were ablaze with light, the valleys below were still in darkness. As the moon turned toward the sun these valleys lost their darkness. In the same manner valleys on earth become filled with light as the sun rises. Galileo could have no doubt that the moon, like the earth, took its light from the sun.

On January 7 Galileo's favorite telescope, one he called

"Old Discoverer," picked up three small stars very close to the planet Jupiter. Galileo thought it odd that he had not noticed them before because they were arranged in a straight line. Two were to the east of Jupiter and one was to the west:

    *   * o *

"I paid them no attention," he wrote later. "But the next night to my great surprise all three had skipped over to the west side of the planet.

EAST   o * * *   WEST

"I wondered how Jupiter could be to the east of three stars when just twenty-four hours before it had been to the west of them. No heavenly bodies, neither stars nor planets, had ever behaved in this strange way before.

"With great interest I waited to see what the next night would bring. Alas, the sky everywhere was covered with clouds. On January 10 I saw my starlets again or rather I saw two of them. The third I supposed had hidden itself behind Jupiter.

EAST   * * o   WEST

"On January 12 all three were again in the sky, now arranged in this way:

EAST   * * o *   WEST

"What could these little bodies be? They could not

be stars for stars do not move through the heavens in that way.

"The next night another surprise awaited me, a fourth starlet:

EAST   *   O * * *   WEST

"There could be only one answer. These were moons racing around the planet just as our moon swings around our planet. At first I had thought I had come upon new stars. Now I knew I had discovered something far more important: a number of small heavenly bodies circling around a larger body."

Wasn't this similar to the plan Copernicus had thought up for the earth and the sun: small planets, including our earth, moving forever around a great sun. Jupiter was the center of a moon system. Why then could not the sun be the center of a planet system? Any man armed with a telescope could now look for himself and see that such a plan was possible in the heavens.

In a book, *The Starry Messenger,* Galileo related the story of his discovery of the moons of Jupiter. The news spread rapidly and far. Wherever a Venetian ship stopped to trade, men heard of the invention of the telescope and of what it had shown in the skies. Within five years the word had reached China.

Everyone wanted one of Professor Galilei's telescopes, and Master Workman Mazzoleni was busy from early morning until late at night. To keep his telescope from shaking,

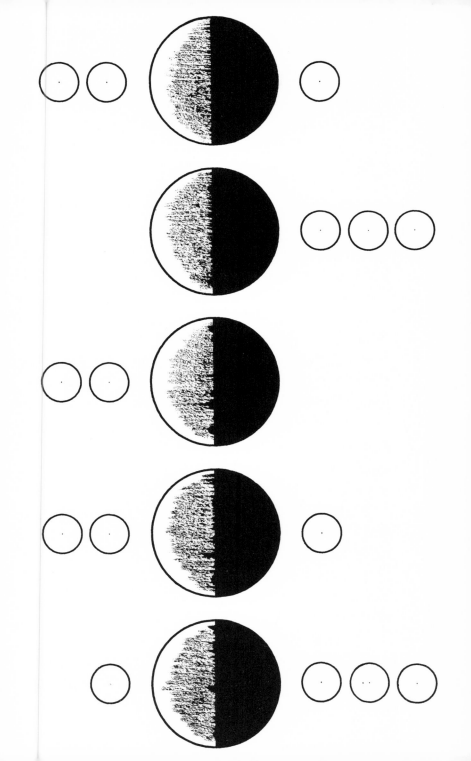

Galileo designed a stand on which it could be supported. The tubes holding the lenses could be drawn in and out to view objects both far and near. Other men began to build telescopes but none were as skillfully made or as powerful as Galileo's.

From France, Italy, Flanders and Germany, the nobility wrote to Galileo asking for one of his marvelous instruments. When she received her telescope the French Queen Marie immediately lay down on her back to view the moons of Jupiter.

"I hear," she wrote to Galileo, "that you are calling them the Medicean Stars to honor the Grand Duke of Tuscany, Cosimo de' Medici. I don't understand why you didn't think of my dear husband Henri first. Please name your next star after him."

"You'd think," Galileo said to Sagredo, "that the stars were getting on line to be named after the crowned heads of Europe."

"Something puzzles me," said Sagredo, "and almost everyone else in Venice too. Why did Professor Galilei, one of the most honored citizens of the Venetian Republic, name his greatest discovery after the ruler of a far-off city? Surely there are great men worthy of the honor closer to home?"

For once Galileo was not completely open with his good friend. He skirted the question. "There will be plenty of other stars," he said.

Among the letters Galileo received was one from his brother Michelangelo. His job in Poland had turned out badly. Then for years he had been out of work until Galileo got him a position as music master to the Grand Duke of Bavaria.

Galileo looked after Michelangelo and his growing family as though he had been his father. He would write again and again and get no reply:

All I ask, Michel, is that you write and give me some news of yourself, your wife and children. You have not answered my last four letters. I'd rather think my letters missed you than that you did not mean to answer them.

Michelangelo, however, always remembered to write when he wanted something for himself. Now he was peeved that the dear brother he loved so much and of whom he so often thought had failed to send him a telescope. He also excused his failure to pay his share of Virginia's dowry:

If I am not a prince, at least I am your brother and it seems strange that you do not wish to please me. God knows that if I haven't sent you money to pay my share of the dowry, it is because I cannot do so. However, if that is what you want I'll go into debt and send it to you.

I don't deny that I spent a lot of money on my last big feast. But don't forget that I had more than eighty guests, not your common folk but people of nobility who expect to be treated well. I do know you would not want your younger brother put to shame.

One thing is certain, you can't say I spend the money on my own pleasure. And have a little pity, Galileo. Why should I work all my life just to provide my sister with a dowry? By the way I'd consider it a great pleasure if you would send me six lutes which I need for playing at court.

Galileo's own family had grown with the passage of time. His second daughter Livia had been born in 1601 and his son Vincenzio in 1604. Galileo was fond of his children. Often after dinner he would sit in the garden with Giovanni Sagredo, watching the heavens, while the young ones and Marina played nearby.

One warm spring evening Sagredo had been peering at the planet Saturn through "Old Discoverer" for a long time.

"You are right," he said at last. "I can make out two moons, one on either side of the planet."

"Something very strange about them though," said Galileo. "I have looked at them a thousand times and yet they never seem to move as proper moons should. If it weren't such an odd thing to say, I'd guess they were fixed in space."

Galileo did not know it but he had discovered the strangest object in the heavens: the rings of Saturn. Through his low-powered telescope they looked like moons. Actually they are three flat bands of billions of tiny pebbles probably made of ice.

Sagredo laughed. "Another discovery to annoy the professors!"

"What annoys me," said Galileo, "is that some of my fellow professors simply refuse to look through my telescope. I said to Professor Libri, 'If you don't believe me, here's my telescope. See for yourself.'

"Do you know what he said? 'How can you expect to see anything in the heavens of which Aristotle said nothing? If this instrument of yours had any real use, Aristotle would have thought of it. I would not look at your moons of Jupiter if I were dying.'"

Sagredo chuckled. "I heard the story. And you said to him, 'Then be sure not to miss them when you get to heaven.'"

"Oh I did find several who were willing to look. But would you believe it, Giovan, they would not acknowledge what they saw with their own eyes! One of them took a long hard look at the moon through my spyglass and then said, 'Um, um, oh yes, my dear Galilei, it does look quite rough, doesn't it. But you see our master Aristotle was right after all. Covering the mountains and cliffs you see is a smooth glass coat you cannot see.'

"Tell me, Giovan, should I have laughed or cried? I said to him, 'Not a bad idea. I'm willing to take it if you will now say that over this smooth coating of yours are other mountains and cliffs all made of this same invisible stuff.'

"Well, he's stopped talking to me. What are we going to do with such people? If the truth cannot be found in an old book, it simply does not exist. My good friend Cesare Cremonino, who earns twice what I do, keeps six horses, two coaches and scores of servants, says no one ever saw anything through my telescope. When I ask him to look, he says that my tricky lenses make him dizzy. Cremonino has written scholarly books about the stars and yet he will not take a good look at them. In a few short months we have learned more than we have ever known about the heavens and yet these teachers at the universities refuse to change their ideas."

Sagredo patted Galileo's hand. "No use getting angry," he said gently. "Cremonino and people like him hold ideas that all mankind has believed for thousands of years. He is certain that the earth belongs in the center of the universe. It is the only place fit for man. 'If the earth were only a second-rate planet,' he says, 'swinging around the sun just like every other planet, man's position would be lowered. God could never have intended to give man a second-rate home.' "

"Such people," said Galileo, "are so anxious that the earth be in the very center of the universe that they play the part of God and put it there. But science cannot give in to people's wishes. Science sees the world *as it really is*. It cannot suit the world to people's ideas."

"I'm afraid you'll never get the professors on your side," said Sagredo. "Why don't you try the Church? Have you spoken to Father Clavius? He's chief mathematician at the Roman college and trusted by the Pope."

"Clavius!" Galileo cried. "Do you know what he said to me? 'If the only way to see the moons of Jupiter is through your telescope, then the moons must be inside the telescope.' "

Virginia, Galileo's favorite child, had come over quietly and sat down next to her father.

"Moons are too big," she said, "to fit inside spyglasses."

Galileo put his arm about her. "It is easier," he said, "to explain the heavens to a child than to—"

Suddenly the garden gate burst open and Brother Sarpi rushed in. He was followed by a man who remained hidden in the bushes.

"I have to talk to you at once, Galileo," Sarpi spoke hurriedly. "Oh, it's you, Giovan. No, stay, you should hear this too. What about the child?"

"Marina," Galileo called, "time for the children to be abed."

After his family had gone, Galileo turned to Sarpi. "What's wrong?" he asked.

"Galileo, my agents have just sent me word from Rome that your name has been placed on the list of the Inquisition."

Galileo smiled. "Is that what brings you here, Paolo? I am a good son of the Church. I have nothing to fear from the Inquisition."

"No laughing matter," Sarpi said sharply. "You are a Copernican and therefore under suspicion."

Galileo patted his telescope. "I have faith in 'Old Discoverer.' It will yet show us such wonders that the Chief Inquisitor himself will not doubt their truth."

"You fool yourself, Galileo. Your scientific wonders mean nothing to the Inquisitors. There is nothing they will not do to stop you."

"But here, Paolo, under the protection of the Great Republic of the Adriatic?"

"Bring me that lantern," Sarpi cried to the man lurking in the shadow of the bushes.

A tall man with heavy shoulders, armed to the teeth, slouched forward.

"Look at this, Galileo!"

Across Sarpi's face from cheek to throat was a long, ugly dagger cut, barely beginning to heal.

"This is my bodyguard, Antonio. Tell them how I got my pencil scratch, Antonio."

"It happened suddenly in an alley behind St. Mark's. These two jumped Brother Sarpi out of the dark. I guess they didn't see me right behind. I slit the first fellow's throat and shook up the other until he told us who sent him. Then I dumped the bodies in the Grand Canal. Made a nice splash too, they did."

"But Paolo," said Sagredo, "you are a sworn enemy of the Inquisition. You don't think they mean to harm Galileo?"

"I have other news," Sarpi responded sadly. "Professor Galilei does not plan to remain long under the protection of Venice. I have been informed that he has asked Cosimo de' Medici for a position at the Ducal Court in Florence. I need not tell you that the Doge is much displeased.

"Now I begin to understand about the Medicean Stars,"

said Sagredo bitterly. "Less than a year ago the Doge gave you a professorship for life and doubled your salary. It was Venice that welcomed you with open arms eighteen years ago and rewarded you with high honors and friendship. Now that you are famous and no longer need us, is this your way of thanking us?"

"I am sorry," said Galileo, "but I am tired of all the foolish things that have been said about me by my fellow professors. I have enlarged the world a hundred, nay a thousand times from what the wise men of all past ages have thought. Still these prized fools shake their heads and tell me the earth cannot move.

"Then I must tell you, too, that I am tired of spending the best hours of my day teaching. The Duke has promised me that in Florence I will be able to give all my time to study and writing. I am no longer a young man and as you know I have not been well.

"I had a strange accident the year I came to Venice. A friend and I were taking a walk in the country. It was a very hot day and we stopped to rest in a house along the road. Our host allowed us to sleep in a room close to an underground cavern from which cool air blew. When I awoke I was very ill and my friend was dead. Since that time I have suffered great pains in my bones which keep me in bed for long periods.

"I want to devote whatever good years I have left to my science. If I leave Venice it is not because I have stopped loving my friends."

"I am thinking only of your good," said Sagredo. "Where in all Italy will you find a way of life that allows you as much freedom to think and to speak as you have here? Cosimo de' Medici, your new master, is a worthy prince. He rules Tuscany now, but who can tell what may happen in the future. Today he defends you against your enemies. But tomorrow another may be in his place who fears their power more than the loss of your friendship."

"I thank you, my dear friend, for speaking so freely to me. But a son of Florence never forgets his city. I long to walk again along the banks of the yellow Arno and cross the Ponte Vecchio. I want to stroll through the market place and hear the speech of my people. At this time of year in Florence the air glows red in the spring sunset. Vespers sound from the bell towers and the work of the day is over. Everyone gathers in the streets and squares—teachers, workmen, artists, doctors, tradespeople. Everyone chatters, gossips, jokes, talks about everything under the sun. I want to wander into the hills which I knew as a boy and see below me, bathed in a gold and orange light, the churches, squares and houses of my city. In short, my dear friends, I am homesick."

"I hope the time never comes," Sarpi said, touching his wound with his fingers, "when you will be sorry that you left Venice."

Chapter 12 / A New Ally

GALILEO RETURNED TO Florence in September, 1610.

The unknown young teacher who had left home eighteen years before returned to his native Tuscany one of the most famous men in Italy. Poets composed lines in his honor. Artists painted his portrait on church walls. Scientists and learned men from all over Europe corresponded with him.

He was hardly a month in the new observatory the Grand Duke built for him before he made another great discovery. One evening he was visited by his good friend, Filippo Salviati, a wealthy merchant of Florence, who had been one of his students at Padua.

"Filippo," Galileo said, "I think I can now prove that at least one of the planets, Venus, goes around the sun, and not around the earth."

"Venus!" said Salviati in astonishment. "But don't the followers of Aristotle point to Venus as proof that the planets do not go around the sun. They say that if Venus did go around the sun, we would see its shape change. Sometimes we would see it full, sometimes half-round, sometimes as a crescent. In other words it would go through phases like the moon. Now Galileo, you have to admit that Venus doesn't change. No man ever saw a half-Venus or a crescent Venus. There's Venus as the evening star shining all by itself in the western sky. Look for yourself."

Galileo smiled slyly. "Filippo, you are right, and for once the professors are right. No man has ever seen Venus change its shape. But then no man has ever looked at it through my spyglass. Come, my friend, you are not one of those who is afraid of what he sees."

Salviati peered through the telescope for a long time. Then a long low whistle of surprise escaped him. "Is that Venus? It looks like a crescent moon!"

Galileo rapidly drew a sketch. "Here's the earth, here's the sun, and there's Venus on her orbit around the sun. To change her shape and size as she does, Venus must go around the sun and not around the earth.

"The professors have insisted that everything must go around the earth. Well here is one planet which positively does not. What are they going to say now?"

"You've stumped them," said Salviati. "Galileo, the time has come for you to go down to Rome and show your discoveries to the Church."

"Just what I have been thinking," said Galileo. "If people will only look through my spyglass, I know they

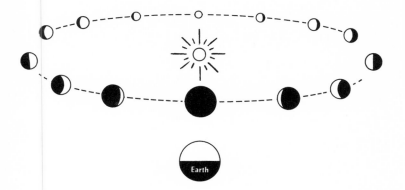

Venus, like all the other planets including the earth, goes around the sun. Because Venus is inside the earth's orbit we see only those parts of Venus that can be seen from this planet. There are times when we see a full Venus, a half Venus, a crescent Venus and when it is closest to us no Venus at all.

When it is full it will look smallest because it is then furthest away. When crescent shaped it will look largest. Before the invention of the telescope no one was able to see these changes in Venus.

will agree with me. I don't care whether they are students, merchants, princes, priests or popes."

"But not professors!" said Salviati.

Galileo was forced, however, to delay his trip to the

great city on the Tiber River. The winter of 1610-11 in Florence was very hard and the pains he suffered became worse.

Salviati had a house in the country outside Florence and Galileo went there to recover from his illness. One January morning Galileo called Filippo to his room. The shutters were drawn tight, the only light coming from a small opening. Next to the window Filippo was able to make out a telescope and behind it a large white board.

"You are supposed to be resting, not working," said Salviati. "What have you there?"

"Oh, a little trick of my own to study the sun without hurting my eyes. Now just let me focus my spyglass."

Almost at once an image of the sun was cast on the board.

Salviati noticed several black spots falling within the outline of the sun.

"I've seen them a thousand times," said Galileo. "I don't know what they are. Call them sunspots if you like. They fall about halfway between the North and South Poles of the sun and move from west to east. Sometimes I've seen as many as twenty or thirty at a time all traveling with one common motion instead of each going about by itself."

"What makes them move?" Salviati asked.

"You have two guesses. Either they move by themselves or else—"

"Or else," said Salviati, "they are part of the sun and it is the sun that is moving and carrying them along just as the earth is moving and carrying her mountains along with her."

"Exactly, my good pupil." Galileo smiled. "They are part of the sun's landscape as it were. They move because the sun is turning.

"These spots prove that the sun spins from west to east just as the earth does. By studying the spots I have discovered that it takes the sun twenty-eight days to turn around once. A day on the sun is almost a month on the earth."

"Your discovery is going to upset a lot of people at Padua. It will bother them more than the Medicean Stars or the phases of Venus. Spots on the sun! Now my dear Professor Galilei, isn't this going a bit too far? Doesn't our master Aristotle say that the heavens are made of a fine material that is perfect and unchangeable? The earth is imperfect, not the sun. Are you trying to destroy the difference between heaven and earth?"

"Bravo, Filippo!" cried Galileo. "I could swear I heard my old friend Cremonino talking. It is true that my discoveries are wiping out the differences between heaven and earth. The sun spins, the moon spins and most likely the earth does too. All the planets swing round the sun; so does the earth. All the planets enjoy the light of the sun; so does the earth. Some of the planets have moons; so does the earth. If we were on the moon it would seem to us that the earth was in the heavens in the company of the stars and the other planets."

"Do you think you'd find life on the moon?"

"I think not. Life needs soil and water and the moon has neither. Besides the moon spins too slowly to keep its surface evenly heated. Every part of the earth gets light and heat from the sun every twenty-four hours. But each side of the moon faces, first, fifteen days of sunlight and then fifteen days of night. If our animals and plants had fifteen days of the sun and then fifteen days of cold and darkness I'm afraid they would not live very long. If life could not exist on earth under those conditions, it could not exist on the moon either."

"The old astronomers," said Salviati, "thought that earth and heaven were separate worlds. But your discoveries have placed the earth out in space among the stars and planets. I never thought I was in heaven already!"

Galileo laughed. "How does it feel?"

In March, 1611, Galileo was well enough to make his trip down to Rome.

Rome was the greatest city of Italy and the capital of the Papal State, ruled by the Pope. The men of the Church proved to be much more open to the new ideas inherent in Galileo's discoveries than the professors in the universities. He was welcomed everywhere.

In the gardens of the Quirinal Palace bishops and cardinals elbowed each other aside in their eagerness to look through Galileo's telescope. For the first time they saw the wonders of which they had heard so much.

A few remained doubtful. One half-blind old man

cackled. "I have read the ancients cover to cover and nowhere do I read anything similar to what you see in your spyglass. What you say are spots must be a weakness of the eyes. Go, my son, lie down and rest."

But most of Rome believed what they saw. Cardinal del Monte praised Galileo. "A statue should be built in your honor."

One of those who came to the Quirinal Palace was Federigo Cesi, son of the powerful Duke of Aquasparta. "I cannot build a statue for you," he said. "But I can invite you to join the Society of the Lynx."

First of the academies devoted to science, the Society of the Lynx had been founded by Cesi eight years earlier. Galileo prized his membership all his life. Through the Society he gained powerful friends who helped defend his views and spread his ideas.

Finally there came a command to visit Pope Paul V. As the head of the Roman Catholic Church and ruler of Rome, the Pope held more power than most kings and emperors.

"Professor Galilei, I have just received a report about your discoveries from my mathematician, Father Christopher Clavius. We will call him in and let him tell you what he told me."

Galileo felt chilled. Only too well did he remember what Father Clavius had once said. He bowed stiffly as the tall, thin-lipped priest entered the hall.

Father Clavius spoke slowly and carefully. "I have

examined Professor Galilei's reports about his discoveries in great detail, including the moons of Jupiter, the phases of the planet Venus and the spots on the sun. I have informed the Holy Father that there can be no doubt as to the truth of these great discoveries. In every case Professor Galilei is completely correct."

Father Clavius was smiling broadly now. Even the Pope seemed to have a twinkle in his eyes.

"And may I at this time," Father Clavius went on, "in the presence of the Holy Father, tell Professor Galilei how sorry I am for a foolish remark I once made."

Galileo left the papal palace glowing with pride and happiness. The battle for science, it seemed to him, had been won. Ah, if only Giovan Sagredo and Paolo Sarpi could be with him now. How quickly they would stop worrying.

As Galileo was about to cross the Tiber Bridge, he glanced to his left. Close to the river rose the dungeon of Castel Sant'Angelo. Terrible tales were whispered of prisoners who had spent long years there only to be murdered by their jailers. There were mysteries and dangers in the great city of Rome of which Galileo knew nothing.

All the way back to Florence the image of a man being burned to death in a public square in Rome kept recurring, try as Galileo would to shake it off. But hadn't the great cardinal said, "A statue in your honor in a public square." Far more pleasant to think of that!

A few months after Galileo returned home Grand Duke Cosimo asked him to dinner.

It was Cosimo's habit to invite leading musicians, artists and scientists to dine with him and talk about their ideas.

It had been an unusually hot day for late September and the talk got around to ice.

"Ice," said one of the guests in a very loud voice, "is heavier than water."

Galileo looked up quickly. The speaker was Lodovico delle Columbe, a Florentine writer who pretended to know much more about science than he actually did. Galileo had a score to settle with him. Just a few weeks before, he and Columbe had agreed to debate on floating bodies. But when the time arrived, Galileo was sick in bed. Lodovico had then spread a story that Galileo was too frightened to face him in public.

"I wonder, my dear Signore Columbe," said Galileo with grave politeness, "why ice floats since, as you say, it is heavier than water."

"Ice," said Columbe in a booming voice that carried all the way up the table to the Grand Duke, "floats because of its shape. Surely, my dear professor, you have heard of Aristotle. He informs us that objects float because of their shape. Even heavy metal will not sink when in the form or shape of foil."

The clatter of silverware along the table stopped. The room was hushed.

"I don't like to disagree with you," said Galileo, still speaking very quietly, "but volume for volume ice is not

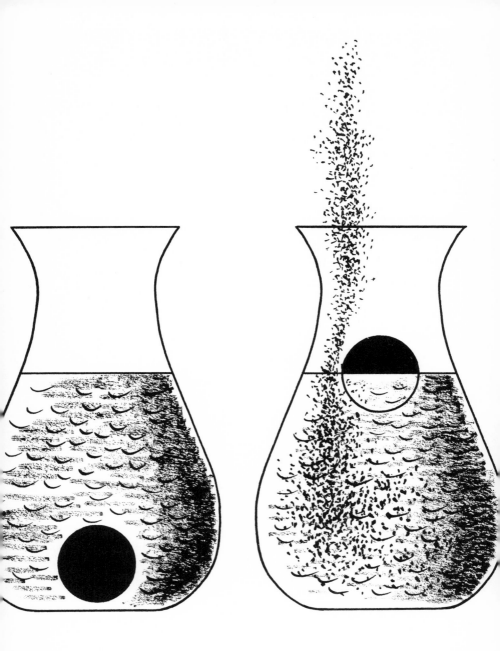

heavier but lighter than water. Fill a bottle with water. Freeze it. The bottle will burst because the ice fills more space than the water. Ice floats because it is lighter than the water from which it was formed."

"My dear professor," Columbe interrupted, "I know you like to say, 'Use your eyes.' May I ask you to use your eyes. Look at the piece of ice floating in the pitcher by your side. Note its wide flat shape. Such a shape resists sinking."

"What kind of shapes *do* sink?"

The questioner was a tall, handsome man with a little pointed beard, sitting at the head of the table on the Grand Duke's right. He was Cardinal Maffeo Barberini, one of the leaders of the Church and often mentioned as the next pope.

"Those shapes sink," said Columbe, "that can slip through the water easily—round shapes, for example."

"What say you, Professor Galilei?" asked Barberini.

"I am sorry," said Galileo, "that we cannot test Signore Columbe's idea with a ball of ice. But I have something else here that may help him change his mind, that is if his mind can be changed."

Galileo took some tallow from a dripping candlestick and rapidly rolled it in his fingers.

"Here we have a ball-shaped object. Will it float or sink? Let us ask Signore Columbe."

"Sink, without a doubt," Columbe said quickly.

"Very well, then, let's try," said Galileo. "And will Signore Columbe, lest he think I have some trick up my sleeve be kind enough to drop it into his glass of water?"

"Hold it high, my dear signore, so that all may see for themselves."

Columbe dropped the ball. "Plunk!" It sank at once to the bottom of the glass.

"If all your experiments, my dear Professor Galilei," said Columbe, "end like this, I can understand why you refuse to debate with me."

Galileo, however, did not seem worried. "Yes, Signore Columbe seems to have won. He says a ball-shaped object will sink. He tries the experiment. The object sinks. He seems to have proved that it is the shape of an object that will decide whether it sinks or not.

"But before we rush to offer our congratulations, let us try one more experiment. Again I ask Signore Columbe to raise his glass. Will he now kindly pour just a little salt into the water."

"Better luck this time, my dear professor," said Columbe, beginning to pour the salt.

"One of us will need the luck," said Galileo sharply, "but not I. Tell me, Columbe, what do you see?"

Columbe did not answer. His mouth had dropped open in amazement. The ball of wax was stirring at the bottom of the glass and now was slowly rising.

Columbe's hand began to shake.

"Easy, Columbe," said Galileo. "Aren't you feeling well? Here, let me hold the glass for you. Keep pouring."

The ball had risen to the surface and was now floating on the top.

"Let us use our eyes, my dear Columbe. Tell me what do you see?"

"A trick of some sort," muttered Columbe.

"Not at all," said Galileo. "Only a law of nature. The ball sank in the glass of pure water not because of its shape but because its weight was greater than that of an equal volume of water.

"What happened when you were kind enough to pour the salt? The water gained weight. Just as soon as the weight of the ball was less than the weight of an equal volume of water the ball rose and floated on the top. Or to put it more bluntly, you would float in water despite your rather well-rounded shape because you weigh less than an equal volume of water."

At this point the guests rose from the table laughing and Cardinal Barberini came over to Galileo.

"A remarkable experiment, Professor Galilei," he said. "I enjoyed every moment of it. I notice you hold a rather low opinion of Aristotle."

"Not of Aristotle," said Galileo, "but his followers, people like Columbe who would rather pull a book from the shelf than find out for themselves. Columbe reminds me of an artist who closes his eyes to nature and spends his whole life copying the pictures of others. Columbe doesn't understand that nature has given us almost two thousand more years of information and observation than she gave Aristotle."

"I, on the other hand, hold a very high opinion of

you," said Barberini. "I have written a few verses which I shall send you. Please accept them as proof of my respect and affection. I hope you will always remember how much I admire a mind as gifted as yours."

Shortly thereafter Galileo wrote to Sagredo in Venice: "We have conquered. The Church, the men of learning and affairs, the nobility, all are on our side!"

Sagredo's reply was strange: "Galileo, you have placed yourself in the lion's jaws!"

Chapter 13 / The Mask

ON THE FIRST day of winter, 1614, Father Thomas Caccini of Florence preached in the Church of Santa Maria Novella. Though the Christmas season was near, this was certainly not a sermon in the spirit of Christmas.

"Mathematics," he thundered, "is an invention of the devil. He who dares to say that the earth moves is an enemy of religion. Is not Professor Galilei guilty of heresy?"

"Heresy!" Caccini's listeners shuddered. Heresy was the worst of all crimes, punishable by death at the stake. So Professor Galilei was a heretic; one never could tell about those scientists with their strange ideas.

"Don't pay any attention to Caccini," advised Galileo's friends. "Laugh it all off. These people are all fools. Haven't you heard? One of Caccini's flock wanted Copernicus thrown into jail. He had to be told the dreadful man died a long time ago."

But Galileo was troubled. Caccini was a fool no doubt.

On the other hand he would never have dared to say what he did if there were not others, more powerful, behind him.

Galileo wrote to Father Luigi Maraffi, Caccini's superior. Maraffi answered at once. He was terribly sorry that anyone could have been so stupid. Rest assured it would not happen again.

A few days later Caccini was at Galileo's door. "I'm told you were a little upset by something I said at Santa Maria Novella the other day. You must have misunderstood what I was trying to say. How could I have meant any harm? You know I have the greatest respect and admiration for you. But tell me, Professor Galilei, isn't it true you believe in this Copernican nonsense?"

Galileo was not taken in by Maraffi's letter or by Caccini's visit. He knew something was in the air. But he wasn't sure what it was. It would all have been clearer to him had he seen the letter Caccini wrote to his brother in Rome:

> *If my plans go through as I expect, I won't be needing your help any longer. I've made some very good friends here in Florence including Lodovico delle Columbe who, as you know, has a special score to settle with Professor Galilei.*
>
> *We meet from time to time, call ourselves The League and work out our next move against him. If we can get the Inquisition moving on this, I'll be the one to get the credit. You'll be proud of your little brother yet. I expect to end up with a cardinal's hat.*

Galileo, however, knew about the League. He even knew the names of some of the members. Some were professors in the universities; a few were in the Church. They had been spreading stories about him which had already reached Rome. But he did not believe that the Church would pay any attention to such troublemakers.

He began to take them more seriously, however, when Benedetto Castelli, his old pupil went to Pisa as professor of mathematics. The moment Castelli arrived he was told that he was never to talk about, teach or even hint at the idea that the earth moved. The topic was forbidden.

The League's power was growing.

Galileo made up his mind to go down to Rome to get the help of the Church and stop the attacks against him once and for all.

He arrived in the Eternal City in December, 1615. An honored guest of the ambassador from Florence, he stayed at the Villa Medici high on the Pincion Hill. When he looked out of his window he had a grand view of the ancient city including the dome of St. Peter's.

On the little mule the Grand Duke had given him, he rode at once to see Prince Cesi, the founder of the Society of the Lynx.

But his good friend did not seem very happy to see him. "My dear Galileo, I beg you, go easy. These are not times to bring up new ideas. I've spoken to Cardinal Bellarmine who is one of the heads of the Inquisition. He agrees with me completely. We must believe the Bible when it tells us that the earth is removed from the heavens and that it is motionless in the center of the universe. If you want to say, however, that the Copernican plan is just a guess that helps you chart the place of the planets in the sky, that's perfectly all right. But I must warn you, do not say it is a fact!"

"And, pray, why not?"

"Because it is contrary to our faith."

"I deny that. If there are a few in the Church who still cling to the idea that the earth is the center of the universe they do so because they do not know any better. All I ask is a chance to talk to them and show them the proofs."

Cesi shrugged his shoulders. "You are a stubborn man. Aren't you aware that you have powerful enemies who are not interested in your proofs?"

"You mean fools like Caccini and Columbe," cried Galileo angrily. "Are they to decide whether the earth moves or not? The professors were bad enough. But at least they knew something about mathematics and astronomy. These idiots hide behind the Church to attack science about which they know absolutely nothing."

"I'm sorry you will not take my advice," said Cesi. "I'll do what I can to arrange meetings with leading churchmen for you."

The battle for science had shifted from the universities to the Church, from Aristotle to the Bible. Galileo had won the first round against the professors. Could he win the second round against the Inquisition?

In Rome that winter he took it upon himself to show that his views were not contrary to religion; rather, they agreed with religion.

"But Professor Galilei," said one churchman, "does not wise King Solomon say in the Bible that the earth is still whereas the sun rises and sets?"

"The Bible," said Galileo, "is the word of God and therefore can never speak an untruth. But let us also remember that the word of God is found not only in the Bible but also in nature. It was God who commanded that the earth should move and go about the sun. Surely God who gave us sense, reason and intellect did not intend us to avoid their use."

"But," said another, "such new ideas may endanger our religion. Some already say you are attacking the Church."

"To use religion to teach an untruth," said Galileo, "is even more dangerous. If we do not tell the truth about the heavens, how will man ever know what God's world is really like. The Bible says:

The heavens proclaim the glory of God
And the firmament showeth his handiwork.

"I am not attacking the Church. I am trying to keep Her from making a great error."

"My son," said an elderly cardinal, "to explain the Bible is the duty of the Church, not yours. If each man were allowed to do so, each man would have his own explanation and perhaps his own religion. Thus heresy would spread."

Galileo answered slowly. "I firmly believe that the Bible was intended to teach us religion, not science. Religion is meant to tell us how to go to Heaven, *not how the heavens go.*"

The old man began to laugh. "Very good, very good,

indeed. 'To tell us how to go to Heaven, not how the heavens go.' I must remember that."

Before a month had gone by everybody in Rome was talking about the new ideas. Everyone heard how Galileo had destroyed the arguments of the other side. By himself Galileo seemed to have turned the tide of public opinion.

All day long a string of visitors came up the Pincion Hill to meet and talk to the famous scientist. Even Caccini called and seemed ready to be friendly. Were Galileo's enemies close to surrender?

Then, at the beginning of February, 1616, came really good news. Father Paolo Foscarini had written a book defending Galileo and the Copernican plan. The book was especially important because it was the first published defense of Copernicus to come from a leading churchman. Victory was in sight. All that was needed was a call from St. Peter's.

The call came on February 26—in the form of an order. Galileo was to report at once to the throne room of Cardinal Bellarmine.

Galileo entered the room expecting to be greeted warmly. Instead he found the Cardinal dressed in his robes of office seated on his throne and surrounded by a group of monks in white and black habits.

"Professor Galilei," said Cardinal Bellarmine, "the eleven Inquisitors of the Holy Office have decided that the idea that the earth moves is both foolish and contrary to the Bible. I must therefore warn you to give up this mistaken idea at once."

Galileo was stunned and for a time could not answer. He felt terribly alone and deserted. Where were all the good friends who could have helped him? Where was Maffeo Barberini who wrote poetry in his honor and then did nothing for him when he needed him most? He thought he had won everybody in Rome to his side. And all the while, the Inquisition had been waiting, ready to pounce on him just when he imagined victory was within his grasp.

Bellarmine spoke up impatiently. "Do you consent to this order of the Holy Office?"

Galileo knew better than to argue with the Inquisition. Once its mind was made up, nothing in the world could change it. He nodded his head.

The Cardinal then stepped down from his throne, put his arm around Galileo and led him aside.

"Don't look so sad, my friend," he said kindly. "You must know how much I and others in the Church admire you. Just between you and me we do not mind your Copernican ideas—that is, if you keep them to yourself, under the rug, as it were. Consider what happens when you allow such notions to spread. Open the window to one error and a thousand fly in. State today that the sun is the center of the world and tomorrow another man comes along and says there are other suns, other worlds, other men on these other worlds and so on and on. No, Galileo, do not smile. That is exactly what a certain heretic said. I know for I, Bellarmine, helped to send him to the stake sixteen years ago."

Galileo said, "If you say that I am wrong, I must agree. I am a good son of the Church."

Bellarmine drew a sigh of relief. "I am happy for your sake that you are so sensible. We would not have enjoyed placing Archimedes on trial for heresy."

"May I ask one question? What of Copernicus' book?"

"I am sorry," Bellarmine answered, "but it will be forbidden until corrected."

The decision of the Inquisition was printed and then sent to all parts of Europe where the rules of the Church were followed. It was read in churches and in the universities. Bookshops and libraries were raided and Copernicus' books were seized. Those who dared hold on to their copies hid them away in secret places.

The printer who had published Foscarini's defense of Copernicus was thrown into jail. Foscarini himself died a short time thereafter under mysterious circumstances.

On the streets men began to look over their shoulders when they talked about science. Who knew but a Caccini might be ready to report them to the Inquisition. Some of Galileo's friends turned aside when they met him face to face. Others cut short their talk as though they did not want to be seen in his company.

Galileo was sick at heart. "I'm a marked man," he said to a loyal friend, Father Giovanni Ciampoli. "Those who once sought my company now flee when they see me."

"Do not give up," Ciampoli said. "Wait and the tide will yet turn. In the meantime you still have good friends— Giovanni Sagredo and Brother Paolo Sarpi in Venice, the Grand Duke in Florence, the great astronomer Johannes Kepler in Germany . . ."

Galileo smiled. "And in Rome my dear friend Father Giovanni Ciampoli!"

Eight years went by and Galileo waited. For eight years he wore a mask, hiding his thoughts and feelings, pretending to believe what he did not believe.

The Inquisition was everywhere, listening to what he said, poking its lean fingers into his mail, questioning his friends. At any moment the dread call might come, the call to report once more to Rome. The last time it had only shown its teeth. The next time . . . "Without a mask," Brother Sarpi had said, "no man may live in Italy."

While Galileo waited in Florence, deep within his mind, out of the Inquisition's reach, he planned the book which some day would tell mankind all he knew about the earth and the heavens.

Galileo rented a small house in Arcetri on the outskirts of Florence and spent a good part of his time taking care of his olive crop and pruning his grapevines. He quickly became an expert at cutting and grafting; farmers came to consult him about their vines.

A half-hour's pleasant walk from his house brought Galileo to the Convent of San Matteo. There his daughters now lived. Both girls had become nuns, Virginia taking the name of Sister Maria Celeste and Livia, Sister Arcangela. Galileo's arrival was the great event of the day. The entire convent was in a flurry.

Sister Maria Celeste was very proud of her parent. She made preserves for her father, laundered his collars, mended his cloak. She treasured Galileo's books, though she did not understand them fully.

Sometimes she received very special permission to go down to Galileo's house to check on his little farm and prepare special dishes for him. Those were days that she remembered all her life. At times she acted as his secretary and copied his papers in her clear and beautiful hand.

Her letters came almost every week. "I am sending you," she wrote, "a few biscuits baked in the shape of a fish and four plums, though I am afraid they may not be perfect. Everyone is so happy since you repaired our window. Mother Superior says I had no right to ask the great Professor Galilei to fix a window as though he were a carpenter. Now I am sorry. Will you forgive me? I have been very busy with the napkins I promised you but now that I come to putting on the fringe I find I need more thread. Could you send us a little. We are so poor here.

"How pleased I am with the letters you send me. Except for you there is no one in the whole world who makes me happy. I continue to pray God to give you health. I hardly notice what little freedom I have here except when I hear that you have been ill. Then I wish—I know I should not say this—that I could come and live in your house. Send me your laundry. And please forgive Vincenzio."

Vincenzio was a great disappointment to his father. Galileo had sent him to his old university at Pisa to read law but the boy wasted his time and money. Yet Galileo could not discipline him or even recognize his faults.

Galileo wrote to Benedetto Castelli asking him to look after Vincenzio:

For his allowance he is not to have more than three crowns pocket money a month. He may consider himself lucky to have as many crowns as I at his age had pennies.

Professor Castelli was shocked. Three crowns was a tremendous sum of money. He shook his head sadly. His friend Galileo could never stop spoiling his family.

In August of 1623 great news came from Rome for Galileo. Cardinal Maffeo Barberini had been elected pope.

Father Giovanni Ciampoli wrote at once: "You'll be amazed by all the changes that are taking place here. Your old friend and pupil Giovanni Ciampoli is now private secretary to the Pope. His Holiness talks of you constantly: 'When is Galileo coming?' he keeps saying. 'He is the one man in all Italy I want to see.' And do you know, Galileo, that he insists I read your books to him at dinner. I think the time has come for you to publish some of your ideas."

At last Galileo could take off his mask.

Chapter 14 / The Proudest Moment

IN THE SPRING of 1624 Galileo and Maffeo Barberini met again. Barberini was now Pope Urban VIII, ruler of the Papal States in Italy, head of the Roman Catholic Church around the world, and one of the most powerful men on earth.

He embraced his old friend with great affection. "I have waited for this moment for a long time," he cried. Then he showered Galileo with gifts—a picture of himself, two medals, one of gold and one of silver, and a gift of sixty crowns a year for Vincenzio.

"I'm afraid my son can't take something he hasn't earned," said Galileo.

The Pope smiled. "Then I give it to you," he said.

"May I," said Galileo, "offer you my latest invention—a microscope. To enlarge any object you place it under the lens on this movable stage."

The Pope peered into the microscope. "I see only a blur," he said.

"Notice," said Galileo, "that there are two tubes, one fitting into the other. Move them and you bring the lens into focus."

"Ah, I see now!" cried the Pope. "A monster as big as a goat!"

"Only a little fly," Galileo corrected. "Does your Holiness see the points at the end of the legs?"

"For the first time," the Pope said, "I understand how flies can walk upside down. They can place those points into the pores of the smoothest surfaces. Your new instrument will enable mankind to see the wonders of the tiny world just as your telescope has allowed us to see the glories of the cosmos."

In the next few weeks Galileo and the Pope held many long and frank talks about the Copernican system. "I can tell you," Urban said, "had it been up to me, Copernicus never would have been forbidden."

It seemed to Galileo that the time was now right to talk about his plans.

"For a long time, Your Holiness, I have been thinking of a book that would tell all I have learned in the course of my lifetime about the heavens and the earth."

The Pope seemed delighted. "I'd be the first to encourage you."

"But what about the Church? Would the Church approve my defending Copernicus?"

"The Church can never approve anything that is contrary to religion," said the Pope. "But should you wish to tell about both the Copernican plan of the universe and the plan of Aristotle and Ptolemy, I don't see any objection. You understand, of course, that the Copernican plan can only be presented as a possibility not as a fact. You might call such a book, let us see, *The Two Chief World Systems."*

"The Two Chief World Systems!" Galileo exclaimed. "A wonderful title!"

Galileo returned to Florence, the Pope's last words to him ringing in his ears: "Your fame will live as long as Jupiter and its moons shall shine in the sky." The visit to Rome had gone better than Professor Galilei had dared hope.

But now that he was away from St. Peter's one small doubt arose to trouble him. The Pope had said nothing about his silence of eight years before, not one word of regret or explanation. Galileo quickly shrugged off the feeling. It was good to know he had such a warm friend in Rome. Now nothing could stand in his way. The tide had really turned.

The Two Chief World Systems. The book began to take shape in his mind.

"Suppose we have a number of people, as in a play, who talk about the two plans for the universe. One of them can be an old-line professor who swears by Aristotle. Another can be a modern scientist who depends on experiment and observation for his ideas. And then we ought to have someone who stands between them, an intelligent citizen who hasn't made up his mind."

Such a design for the book would allow him to give

both sides without himself taking sides. There was a great deal of work ahead. The book would take at least five years.

But Galileo's old illness returned and the book had to be put off repeatedly. To add to his troubles his brother's wife and seven children came to stay with him.

Michelangelo had been complaining again. "You're rich," he wrote from Germany, "a friend of popes and princes. Why should I not be as lucky as you? And please stop bringing up that dowry. That was years ago.

"But I'm a forgiving brother. I'll send the family to you. My wife Anna will be your housekeeper and my children will be a comfort to you in your old age. It will be helpful to me too, because I won't have to support them for a time."

Michelangelo's children were far from a comfort to Galileo. They were badly spoiled and Anna was no housekeeper.

From Benedetto Castelli in Pisa, Galileo continued to receive bad reports about Vincenzio. Despite his huge allowance, Vincenzio was so short of cash that Castelli had to buy his shoes for him.

The excitement at home and worries about his son were too much for Galileo and in the autumn of 1628 he became so ill that he seemed on the verge of death. This led Michelangelo to send him the following note:

I'm pleased to know you are better for I tremble to think of what would have happened to my dear

Anna had you died. You say my oldest son doesn't obey. I don't understand; he was fine as long as he was with me. He certainly did not get his bad ways from his father. My dear brother, you say you have your troubles. Believe me, I have mine too.

A few months later Michelangelo himself appeared in Florence. No, he wasn't going to leave his dear family with Galileo another day. The servants had not treated his wife with respect. Why had Galileo tried to get his son a place as a page at the Ducal Palace?

"It is more fitting," he said, "that the son of Michelangelo Galilei should be served rather than that he should serve others. You forget, my dear brother, that we come of a noble family. Rather than getting him a job you should have tried to get him a pension so that he could have stayed at home and practiced the lute. The poor child has forgotten all I taught him."

Galileo was too ill to care one way or the other. He sighed with relief when his brother packed up the whole family and left for Munich.

They were hardly out the door when Vincenzio arrived, having at last graduated from the university. Instead of seeking a job, however, he stayed at home, pretending to help Galileo with his scientific work. When Sister Maria Celeste sent the convent clock to be repaired, Vincenzio tried his hand at it. He puttered around for a while and then returned it in worse shape than before. He spent most of his time idling about the house. Galileo was silent. Himself the son of a kind and loving father, he could never find fault with his own children.

Despite illness and family troubles, Galileo at last got his book started. He wrote simply and directly so that every fairly well-informed reader could follow him. There were three people in it, his old friends Salviati and Sagredo and a character called Simplicio or Simple-Mind. Salviati would be the scientist who speaks for Galileo. Sagredo would stand for the alert open-minded citizen. Simplicio, modeled on all the foolish professors Galileo had known, would be the stubborn blind follower of Aristotle. He would never believe anything that could not be found in an ancient book covered with dust.

"And I'm writing it in Italian," Galileo said to Vincenzio.

"But Father, all serious books nowadays are written in Latin. The universities are not going to buy a book in a language ordinary people understand."

"Exactly," said Galileo. "The professors will not read me but what you call ordinary people will. People think books on science are way above their heads because they cannot read the language in which they are written. I believe they can make out the new ideas in science just as readily as the learned men in the universities. For that reason I'm trying to make my book entertaining and interesting."

Vincenzio yawned. He had no more interest in science than in the law.

While he worked on the book, Galileo kept in touch with Rome. He had suffered enough for the cause of science; he was not going to suffer again. His friend Father Thomas Campanella had only recently come out of jail. He had been confined for twenty-seven years after having attacked the ancient authorities. Galileo had no intention of becoming a martyr. He was going to be absolutely safe this time.

The first step was to get a license for the publication of the book. Not only in Italy, but in most countries, a book could not be published without the permission of the state. In this way a government could censor what was written and choke off any ideas of which it did not approve.

At the beginning of 1630 the time seemed right. One of Galileo's old students, Father Ricciardi, had been made chief censor of the press. Benedetto Castelli had been called to Rome from Pisa to take the place of Father Clavius who had died. Thomas Campanella was now an adviser to His Holiness.

"Come down to Rome at once," Ciampoli wrote. "A thousand friends are here to help you."

In March the Convent of San Matteo gave Galileo a big farewell dinner; Galileo himself provided the food and drink. Everyone crowded around, wishing him godspeed and asking for favors. "Surely," said Mother Abbess, "such an old friend of His Holiness can ask for a little charity for our poor convent."

Sister Maria Celeste looked troubled. "You seem so

frail, Father. Must you make the journey at this time of year? I hear the Plague rages in the towns between here and Rome. Promise you will be careful. Eat these fresh eggs for love of me, and take along this broth I made of the old rooster you sent last week."

Later, on the way to Rome, Galileo recalled how his daughter looked at their farewell—so aged and worn and yet she was still a young woman. She was the only one in his whole family who really loved him. Should she be taken from him . . . but he put the thought away.

In Rome things could not have gone better. A few unimportant changes were made in the book and the Pope himself suggested the closing argument. The Chief Censor in Florence was directed to approve publication.

On July 3, 1632, *The Two Chief World Systems* saw the light of day. That morning Galileo went down to the Ducal Palace and presented the first copy to young Ferdinando who had succeeded his father Cosimo II as Grand Duke of Tuscany. It was the proudest moment in Galileo's life.

Everywhere the work was received with tremendous praise. It was sold out at once. A friend wrote:

I hardly had time to glance at it before it was snatched from me and lent to another. Today no sooner did I get it back by main force than I was begged by a host of others to let them have it. Galileo, you are admired above all the learned men of our age.

From all over Europe came messages of congratulation and good will. But from one man, the man from whom Galileo wanted most to hear, Maffeo Barberini, Pope Urban VIII, came no word at all. Not a letter, not a note, not even a chance remark.

"Perhaps," thought Galileo, "it is the Plague which is holding up his message to me. Or perhaps the great wars abroad keep him so busy. I know I shall hear from him."

Then suddenly on August 1 word came.

Early that morning agents of the Inquisition swooped down on the shop of Landini, bookseller of Florence and publisher of *The Two Chief World Systems.*

"The Holy Office hereby commands you to stop all printing and sales of *The Two Chief World Systems* by Galileo Galilei and hand over to us all copies now in stock."

"But honored sirs," Landini stammered, "I have not a single copy left. They are all sold out, sirs, every one."

Chapter 15 / The Knock on the Door

AT FIRST GALILEO was overcome by the news of the
banning of his book. How could it have happened? He
had carefully followed every rule. He had the approval
of the Censor. Was it possible that his enemies were so
strong that they could sway the highest leaders in the
Church?

Galileo went to see the Grand Duke, and he in turn
told his ambassador in Rome, Francesco Niccolini, to call
on the Pope. But the moment Niccolini brought up Galileo's name, Urban VIII flew into a fury.

"Your fine Galileo," he cried, "has dared to meddle
with things he should best have left alone."

"But Your Holiness," said the ambassador, "my master,
the Grand Duke, does not understand. Did not the book
have the approval of the Church and of you?"

"We were tricked," the Pope said. "Our own secretary
Ciampoli tricked us."

"But did not the Censor, Father Ricciardi, grant the license after going over the book again and again."

"He was fooled just as we were by insincere speeches."

"But how can you forbid a book which on its title page bears the name of the Grand Duke of Tuscany?"

"What of it? We have forbidden books which bear our name!"

"You will agree, Your Holiness, this is a most serious matter. Let Galileo be told of the charges against the book so that he may have a chance to answer."

"I thought you were better informed," the Pope said. "The Holy Office makes no charges. It only announces its judgment. You think, my friend, this is a serious matter. You may tell your master that worse may be in store for your scientist. Let him take care he is not called before the Inquisition. He was once my friend and we often sat at the same table. May God forgive him!"

Niccolini reported back to the Grand Duke and his advisers.

"I could do nothing with the Pope. He's a changed man. He's gone up to his palace at Castel Gandolfo and shut himself in. All the roads are heavily guarded and no one is admitted without being searched. He lives in constant fear that someone is going to poison him. He sees enemies at every hand."

"But what can we do for Galileo?" said Ferdinando.

"At this time, nothing! Keep out of the matter altogether. We dare not defy the Church."

The Grand Duke took his ambassador aside.

"Tell me, Francesco, what is the real reason for the banning of the book?"

"Exactly what I've been trying to find out," said Niccolini. "No one knows. The Inquisition keeps its secrets well. One thing is certain. Many are troubled because Galileo wrote in our native language. Anyone who reads can now learn the arguments in favor of a moving earth. They say he has poisoned the minds of the common people.

"Others say he did not fairly present the ideas of Aristotle. It is true that he gives the arguments for both sides. But who can doubt that Salviati is right and that Simplicio is silly and childish."

Ferdinando smiled. "He certainly makes a fool of Simplicio. He is outargued and outwitted at every turn."

Niccolini lowered his voice. "Galileo's enemies are spreading the rumor that Simplicio is the Pope!"

Ferdinando was shocked. "A horrible untruth," he cried. "Galileo has always looked upon Barberini as a dear friend whom he respects and loves."

"True enough, but in his present condition the Pope is ready to believe almost any story."

Two months of uncertainty and waiting went by for Galileo. From Rome there was no news at all. None of his friends seemed to know what was going on. Unfortunately, Prince Cesi, who could have been of great help, had recently died. Benedetto Castelli had been banished from Rome.

At home Galileo grew more troubled. Sister Maria Celeste tried to cheer him up.

"You'll see," she said. "You'll find it was all a mistake."

Galileo shook his head. "Maria Celeste, I think I am being watched. The noise in the garden last night!"

"Only some children who tried to steal a few vegetables."

"Perhaps, but should it happen that I am taken away, certain friends of mine may call on you. Give them my keys."

"Father, please do not talk that way. I pray for you night and day."

One afternoon in October, 1632, there was a loud knock on the door. Standing in the gateway was the Inquisitor of Florence and two of his agents.

"Galileo Galilei," he intoned, "in the name of the Holy Office we hereby order you to appear in Rome within thirty days before the Commissary General. Do you consent?"

"On what grounds am I charged?" Galileo asked.

"That is not for us to say. Do you agree? If you do, we ask that you sign this paper."

"I willingly obey the order," said Galileo quietly. "I am innocent of any wrongdoing."

But Galileo became very ill and had to ask for a delay. In December the Inquisitor visited Galileo and found him in bed attended by three doctors. The Inquisitor reported

to Rome: "He is very sick; his pulse is weak. If he is forced
to travel at this time, his life will be in danger."

Rome's answer was brief: "If he does not come volun-
tarily, he is to be bound and carried to Rome in irons."

Ill as he was, Galileo rose from his bed and said he
was leaving at once. He would never allow them to drag
him to Rome.

Niccolini spoke to Galileo on the eve of his going. "I
am sorry my master can do so little for the greatest scientist
in Europe. He is not like his father Cosimo. He is a very
young man and fears that the Papal States might declare
war upon us. In Rome I will continue to do what I can for
you. Be of good cheer."

Niccolini looked about him and then whispered, "I
understand you had a visitor a few nights back from a
certain northern city."

Startled, Galileo raised his head from his couch.

Niccolini smiled. "Do not worry, your secret is safe
with us. We understand he offered you the freedom and
safety of the Venetian Republic."

Tears came to Galileo's eyes. "Yes, he told me I could
have my old position back at Padua; my book could be reprinted despite the ban."

"I dare not speak openly," said Niccolini. "But I think
a trip to the north would be better for your health than a
journey southward."

Galileo shook his head. "I am deeply moved that those
in Venice whom I deserted twenty years ago still think so

well of me that they are ready to defy the Inquisition for my sake. But I have never turned my back on a fight. I cannot run out on what I believe. You see, my friend, deep down in my heart I still think I can bring Rome over to the new science."

"You deserve everything good," said Niccolini. "We love and admire you very much. But there is nothing more that we can do for you in Florence. For your journey the Grand Duke will supply a litter and a guide. Godspeed."

On January 20, 1633, Galileo began his fateful last journey to Rome. The weather was bleak and cold. The Plague or Black Death had struck the towns south of Florence and everywhere the country people were terrified of strangers. From hilltop villages church bells continually tolled the death of those who had been carried away. Quarantine stations were set up along the roads. When Galileo arrived at last at the gates of Rome, he was kept outside the walls for twenty days.

On the afternoon of February 13, he was carried into the city, a prisoner of the Inquisition. Never again during his lifetime would he be able to move about freely. At the special request of the Grand Duke, Galileo was allowed to go to the home of the Florentine ambassador. There he would remain until his jailers sent for him.

Prisoner of the Inquisition! Only a very bold or foolish man would dare to see Galileo or even write to him. Fear of the Inquisition filled the hearts of many men. It was like a stone wall about him.

All those who had helped Galileo in the past suffered. Ciampoli was dismissed from his post as private secretary to the Pope. Ricciardi, the Censor, was disgraced and ordered out of the Papal States.

Niccolini, alone, stood by Galileo.

Galileo's courage rose now that the time had come for a confrontation.

"I'll prove my innocence the moment the trial begins," he said. "The Inquisitors are men like other men. Let them see the truth and they will dismiss the charges."

Niccolini could not bring himself to tell Galileo what he faced. A prisoner of the Inquisition did not know what the accusations against him were until he was declared guilty. He never saw the witnesses against him or got a chance to challenge what they said. He would be taken out for questioning again and again until he was no longer certain what was true and what was false.

If he shouted over and over—"I am innocent. Before God, I swear I am innocent!"—they told him he lied and that they had means of making him tell the truth. Then they led him into the torture chamber and showed him the instruments of torture. If he was still stubborn, they stripped off his clothes. But why go further? Long before this step was taken most prisoners had cried their guilt to the skies. On bended knee they begged to be told what crimes they had committed so that they might confess their sins and accept their punishment.

How could Niccolini tell this to Galileo? He could

only say: "To try to defend yourself and insist upon your innocence might not be wise at this time. Probably all they want is a statement from you about the motion of the earth or some such nonsense. Go along with them or I cannot answer for what might happen."

Hearing these words, Galileo fell into a mood of black despair. For the first time he realized that he was caught in a trap from which there was no escape.

On April 16 came the order to transfer Galileo to the prison of the Inquisition. The end was now in sight.

THE LONELINESS IS worst of all.

Cut off from his friends and family, feeling deserted by the entire world, a man sooner or later gives in. After months of being by himself, except for his grim jailers and those who call to question him, he begins to feel: "Why continue the terror? Confess to anything just to get it over with. They don't want the facts from you. They never would have jailed you if their minds were not already made up. They are holy men, men of learning and wisdom. Do you dare to say *they* are wrong and you are right?"

The Inquisition was like no other court. It was prosecutor, judge, jury and witnesses, all in one. It made its own rules. From its verdicts there was no appeal. In its hands even a great saint like Joan of Arc broke down and confessed sins she had not committed, betrayed what she most truly believed.

Once the prisoner admitted his guilt, the nature of the

trial changed. The Inquisition had been proved right once more. It forgave the sinner. He was now safe from torture and death. But he did not go free. Set him free and what example would there be for other evil-doers? He was therefore sentenced to the prison of the Inquisition, often for the rest of his days on earth.

Galileo was called to his first questioning in April, 1633. Then as the spring went by he was repeatedly recalled. Gradually he picked up what they wanted of him. It was like going to school all over again, the Inquisition the teacher and Galileo the pupil.

Little by little the lesson was planted in his soul: "Your life has been a lie. Your experiments, your discoveries, have been false, your books a mass of untruths. You thought you were a good son of the Church. Galileo, you were a heretic all the time.

"We know everything about you. For years our agents have looked over your shoulder. Venice cannot help you. The Grand Duke is only a frightened boy. Your beloved daughter is ailing, sick for news of you. Why are you so stubborn? You know we have wormed the truth out of men far younger and stronger than you. You thought you could change the opinions of the universities and of the Church. In your vanity you dared to dream that all by yourself you could overturn the ancient sacred plan of the universe. Look upon yourself now, foolish man, and admit that you have lost.

"Tell us what we want you to say and we will be

easy with you. Throw yourself on our mercy. Say it was false pride that made you teach the idea of a moving earth.

"Give in, Galileo Galilei, give in!"

Galileo's only relief during his horrible days in the prison of the Inquisition came from the letters of Maria Celeste:

> *Be of good heart, dear father, and do not give way to grief. I have told no one what has happened, hoping to keep my troubles to myself. Who knows, as I write these lines, your worries may be over and you are free once more. I wonder at Vincenzio's not having written. I am sure the poor boy must have some good reason. There are two plump pigeons in the dovecote waiting for you to come and eat them, there are beans in your garden waiting for you to gather them and your tower is sorry for your long absence.*
>
> *Your little mule has become so proud she will be ridden by none but her master. She bucked poor Geppo but nicely when he tried to get on her back. I should gladly enter a worse prison if in doing so I could set you at liberty.*

No letters at all came from Vincenzio but one did come from a friend who had given him a job and who probably did not know where Galileo was.

"Would you kindly tell your boy to tend to business and not waste his time playing with tuning forks and some such inventions? Let him do his puttering after working hours and not during the business day. It it weren't for you, I'd ask him to go."

On the first day of summer, 1633, after almost three months of questioning, Galileo was called before his judges. His voice trembling, he said, "I am here in your hands; do with me as you please. I will say what you wish me to say."

But the Inquisitors were not satisfied. "That is no answer. Speak the truth or other methods will be used. Do you still hold to the Copernican opinion?"

Galileo answered, "I am here to obey." Then he added, each word being wrung out of him: "I no longer hold to the Copernican opinion!"

In the entire history of science no man, perhaps, ever suffered as much for his beliefs. For fifty years of his working life Galileo was forced to spend much of his time defending himself against the hatred and envy of his enemies. Undoubtedly there was plan and purpose in this for they thought to tire him out and drive him from the field. Failing to defeat him in fair battle, they called upon the Inquisition to do what they could not do. Galileo had destroyed forever the whole scheme of the universe in which they believed. With devastating scorn and wit and unanswerable scientific demonstrations, he had proved that almost everything they taught about heaven and earth was a sham. Little wonder they were so bitter.

From the day Galileo made his first discovery, he withstood, almost alone, the full weight of public opinion and of the universities bearing down on him. For thirty-three years the fate of Giordano Bruno haunted his dreams. Now, a tired old man, broken in body and spirit, he sank to his knees and confessed the sins he had not committed.

But the Inquisitors wanted more than a whispered admission within the shadowed and silent halls of the Holy Office. They wanted Galileo to taste the final shame of a public confession in the full light of the noonday sun.

On Wednesday morning, June 22, they entered his cell and dressed him in the long white shirt of the confessed sinner. Then they paraded him, sick and dazed, through the streets of the Eternal City to the Church of Santa Maria Supra Minerva in the heart of Rome. In the presence of his judges and witnesses he was forced to his knees and the sentence read:

"Whereas you, Galileo Galilei, aged seventy years, son of the late Vincenzio Galilei of the City of Florence, having written a book called *The Two Chief World Systems* in which you defend the idea that the earth moves around the sun, we call upon you to hate, curse, and attack your error and your heresy and every other error or heresy that is contrary to the teachings of the Church. We also command that the book be forbidden. We order that you pray for forgiveness for the next three years. And as an example to others we sentence you to the prison of the Holy Office as long as it shall so please us."

Galileo's body was torn by pain. The pain in his knees

was becoming unbearable. But his jailers were not through. A paper was thrust in his face, and gasping for breath, he read:

"I, Galileo Galilei, aged seventy years, son of the late Vincenzio Galilei of Florence, kneeling before you most famous Inquisitors, having with my own hands touched the Holy Bible, swear that I have always believed and with God's help will always believe what is taught by the Church. I hereby hate, curse and attack the false idea that the earth moves. I swear that in the future I will not in speech or in writing say anything that will cast any doubts on my beliefs. And finally should I know of any heretic or of any person who I think is a heretic I will tell the Holy Office at once. So help me God!"

Copies of the sentence were read in churches and universities throughout Europe. In Florence, Galileo's best friends were called to the Church of Santa Croce under pain of punishment and forced to listen to his disgrace. Even in Padua where so many honors had been showered on him in years past the teachers and students were brought together to hear the sentence.

The Inquisitors raided libraries and bookshops hunting down *The Two Chief World Systems.* The black market price of the book jumped to the equivalent of almost one hundred dollars. No man dared protest lest suspicion fall on him too. A great fear gripped the entire learned world.

One July morning, before dawn, Sister Maria Celeste

heard a tap on her convent window. Two old friends of Galileo's stood outside.

"The Inquisitors are busy in the neighborhood," they whispered. "Before he went to Rome, Galileo told us to remove anything from the house that could be used against him."

"The news of his sentence," said Maria Celeste, "has gone through my heart. I can no longer eat or sleep with worry about him. Here are the keys. Do with his papers as you see fit."

All three knew they were in great danger for they were consciously hindering the work of the Inquisition. Possibly at this time Sister Maria Celeste destroyed all the letters Galileo had written to her to keep them from the hands of the Holy Office.

In Rome Galileo was held in prison for another week. Then he was placed under house arrest and in late July turned over to Archbishop Ascanio Piccolomini of Siena. The Archbishop promised the Holy Office that he would take strict charge of his prisoner and not permit him to see anyone.

But from the moment Galileo arrived in the Archbishop's palace, he was treated not as a prisoner but as an honored guest. All day a steady stream of visitors flocked to see him. Ascanio Piccolomini was an old student of Galileo's and a trusted friend.

"You are placing yourself in great peril for the sake of a confessed heretic," said Galileo.

"In my eyes," said Piccolomini, "you are no heretic but the first man in the world. You have been most unjustly used, and I care not who hears what I say."

"My name is erased from the book of the living," said Galileo. "I must remain silent for the rest of my life about the one message I can give to mankind. On my knees, my fingers touching the Holy Bible, I sinned, I swore to a lie; I said that which I knew was not true."

"If your name is clouded, it is but for a short time. It will soon regain its former brightness. Take courage, my friend, from this night sky."

The two men gazed at the heavens bright with stars.

A wisp of a smile played on Galileo's lips. "For a while there in Rome," he said, "I began to doubt it myself. But the earth *does* move."

Chapter 17 / The Gold Chain

IN FEBRUARY OF 1634 Galileo was permitted to leave Siena and return to his little house in Arcetri, outside Florence.

Maria Celeste was at the door to greet him. "I have so longed to see you, my lord," she cried. "When you were in Rome I said to myself, 'If he were but in Siena!' When you were in Siena, I said, 'Would that he were here in Arcetri!' Since you went away, my life has been one long prayer for your freedom."

Tears came to the old man's eyes. "I am not free," he said. "I carry my bonds with me wherever I go. I may never leave this house except to go to church or visit you at the convent. I may never allow more than two visitors in my home. I can no longer lecture or talk with a group of people. Worst of all, I have sworn to turn over to the Inquisition those who believe what I have taught. Oh yes, weekly I must recite the prayers for forgiveness."

164

Maria Celeste knelt by her father's side. "I will take that part of your sentence upon myself. It will save you the trouble of remembering them."

But Galileo did not smile. He looked at his daughter long and intently. Then he took her face in his hands.

"My eyes have been troubling me of late so that I no longer know whether I see truly or not. But it seems to me that you are not looking well, my child. Have these months been difficult for you?"

"I am used to illness," said Maria Celeste as lightly as she could. "I do not make much of it seeing that it is the Lord's will. But come to table. Two plump pigeons are on the fire begging you to eat them."

It was Sister Maria Celeste's last visit to Galileo's house. She grew so weak that she could no longer bake for him or launder his silk cuffs and collars as she once had done.

Worried about his daughter's health, Galileo himself became ill. He wrote to Rome several times asking to be allowed to visit his doctors in Florence. But he received no answer.

In April a message arrived from the convent. Galileo was to come at once. Mother Abbess met him at the gate.

"God's will be done!" she cried. "Sister Maria Celeste is dead. Her last words were for you. When you left for Rome she fell into a deep sorrow and she never recovered."

The terrible news ringing in his ears, Galileo did not know how he managed to get back to his house. From the day he had returned from Siena he had known she was very sick. But he had refused to recognize the seriousness of her condition. Thinking of Maria Celeste had helped him even in his blackest hours in the prison of the Inquisition. And now she was taken from him.

Suddenly a voice boomed in his ear. "Galileo Galilei, the Holy Office is much displeased."

Galileo looked up startled. At the door of his house stood the Inquisitor of Florence.

The Inquisitor went on. "The Holy Office is much displeased with your request for leave to see your doctors in Florence. You are hereby ordered not to ask again either directly or through your friends in Rome. Otherwise you will be returned to the dungeons of the Holy Office in chains."

Overcome by grief and sorrow, Galileo said not a word. Nothing could touch him any longer: torture, imprisonment or death itself. Nothing seemed to matter any more.

That night Galileo woke with a start. It seemed as though someone were calling him for help. It was the voice of his little daughter Virginia. For years to come, dreams about Maria Celeste would continue to haunt him.

Desperately seeking to free himself of the shock of her death, Galileo returned to his scientific work and to a problem that had interested him almost from the first day he had looked at the moon through his telescope.

The moon turns slowly on its axis. Unlike the earth which completes one turn in one day, the moon requires twenty-eight days. This is just about the time it takes the moon to circle once around the earth. As a result the same side of the moon always faces the earth.

"But that is not exactly true," Galileo said to his son Vincenzio, who had come to live with him. "Men have looked at the moon millions of times and thought they were always seeing exactly the same side. I have discovered that as the moon moves it jounces a bit. We can therefore see regions just beyond the edges of the side facing us. It is as though a man moving in a circle around us always kept facing us. But as he moves about us he turns his head very slightly from side to side and up and down. In other words the moon has a kind of rocking movement or libration. Because of this movement we see a bit more than half the moon."

Vincenzio yawned. His father's discovery did not interest him. There did not seem to be any money in it. "Now, Father, why don't you try your hand at helping ships find their location at sea? The Dutch government is offering an enormous prize, enough to make you rich for life."

Galileo smiled. Of what use was vast wealth to a sick and aged prisoner?

But the *problem* did interest him. Ships found their position north and south of the equator by sighting the North Star. But once out of sight of land they had no accurate means of knowing their east-west location. More than one crew starved to death while their ship wandered aimlessly about the ocean seeking its home port.

Galileo drew up an outline for finding a ship's longitude; that is, its east-west position, with the help of Jupiter's moons. The success of his plan depended on his being able to figure out the movement of the moons with great accuracy. But his eyes were getting worse and it was only a question of time before his sight would be gone. Nevertheless he decided to work on the idea as long as he could. The Medicean stars had given a clue to the nature of the universe. How wonderful it would be if they could now help sailors chart the vast and unknown sea.

The Dutch government was thrilled to hear from the great Professor Galilei and named four commissioners to call on him. But Galileo knew what he was risking if he received them. The Inquisition would quickly use the visit as an excuse to return him to Rome. He therefore wrote to the commissioners and asked them not to come. The Dutch government, however, was not easily discouraged.

Early in 1638 two visitors appeared to pay what seemed to be a friendly call. They were the Ebers brothers, Dutch merchants who had lived in Florence for many years. They asked the usual questions about Galileo's health and chatted for a while about the weather. Then the older Ebers took a letter out of his pocket and began to read:

"Noble Galileo Galilei, Professor of Mathematics and Astronomy, famed throughout all of Europe for your discoveries: Greetings! The Dutch Government is honored and happy that you are working on a plan for taking longitude at sea through observation of the moons of Jupiter. We wish to inform you that if it is successful you will never have any cause to complain of the reward we will offer you. In the meanwhile as a mark of our respect for your learning and wisdom may we beg you to accept this gold chain."

Galileo's trembling hands reached for the gold chain but he did not seem able to reach it.

Suddenly the two visitors realized that Galileo was completely blind. They put the chain into his hands.

"May I tell you," Galileo said slowly, "how grateful I am for the honor you do me, a sick old man no longer of any use to himself or to science. Your letter I will keep but I must ask you to take back the chain. Owing to my blindness I fear that I shall never be able to complete my plan. Besides it would not please my jailers that a sinner like me should receive such a great honor."

Chapter 18 / The Visitor

BLIND, ENFEEBLED GALILEO GALILEI lived out his last years in his little house in Arcetri. Too weak to do anything for himself and removed from his friends and students, he was cared for by an unwilling son.

The Inquisitors kept up their strict watch. They knew who his visitors were, how long they stayed and what they said. Their agent was Vincenzio whom they compelled to spy on his own father.

The all-powerful Holy Office, in whose presence princes and nobles trembled, was itself afraid of this feeble old man. They had forced him to get down on his knees and confess his great discoveries a lie. They had burned his books and silenced his followers. Yet they feared that his ideas would one day wipe out the puny world of Ptolemy in which they still believed.

The Inquisition could stop Galileo's tongue but not his thoughts. Despite blindness and age, he continued his scientific work until the day he died. For a long time he had thought of a book in which he would sum up everything he had learned about what we today call the science of physics. It would include such subjects as motion, mechanics, sound and light. He called the book *The Two New Sciences*. Again we meet Sagredo, Salviati and Simplicio. But this time instead of arguing about the heavens they talk about the nature of ballistics, the speed of light, the strength of materials.

Since there was no chance that a book written by Galileo could be licensed in Italy, he arranged in July, 1638, to have it printed in Leyden, Holland. To avoid further trouble with the Holy Office, he pretended that it had been stolen from him and published without his permission.

The Two New Sciences is one of the great landmarks in the history of science. Galileo did not announce any startling discoveries as he did in *The Starry Messenger*. But he did describe what is known as scientific method, the basis for most of the great discoveries which were to be made in future centuries. With this book modern science was born.

Let us take two examples from the book:

Galileo returned to the problem of falling bodies, a topic which had interested him ever since his student days at Pisa. In addition to actual experimentation he made use of scientific reasoning to work out the laws for objects in a free fall.

"Suppose," says Salviati, "we drop two stones, one weighing eight pounds and the other four. According to Aristotle, the first being twice as heavy will travel twice as fast as the second. If that were true what would happen if we fastened the two weights together. Would the four-pounder have a dragging or slowing effect upon the heavier stone? Certainly, a silly thought! Well then, let's say that since the two stones are now combined they ought to travel with the speed of their combined weight, twelve pounds. Which leads us to a further foolishness: If you put together two slow-moving stones somehow or other you get a faster-moving stone.

"There is only one way out of our difficulty: to say that all stones, whether four, eight, twelve or any number of pounds, fall at the same rate of speed from the same height. Does this rule agree with actual experimentation? It does. All objects fall at the same rate provided they are heavy enough to overcome the resistance of the air. In fact if we could remove the air a feather would keep pace with a cannon ball."

Galileo then came very close to our modern definition of gravity. Objects fall, he said, not because of their heaviness, but because they are naturally impelled toward a common center. On this globe the common center is the center of the earth.

Elsewhere in *The Two New Sciences* Galileo wondered about the speed of light.

Simplicio, who as usual speaks for Aristotle, is certain that the movement of light is instantaneous, that is, it needs no time at all to travel.

"When a cannon is fired," he says, "we see the flash at

once no matter how far away we are. The sound, on the other hand, reaches our ears only after some time goes by."

"I'd hardly call that proof," says Sagredo, "that light travels instantaneously. It merely tells me that sound travels more slowly than light."

"I once worked on an experiment," says Salviati, "to find out whether light needs time to travel. You set two men two to three miles apart, each holding a lighted lantern. The first uncovers his light. The moment the second man sees the signal he uncovers his. Then the two move eight to ten miles apart and send their light messages back and forth to each other. Now if you could notice that with the greater distance the signaling is slowed up, then you would have proof that light needs time to travel."

"Have you tried the experiment?" asks Sagredo.

"Only for short distances. I could not tell whether light moved instantaneously or with extreme rapidity. It may be that light travels so quickly that we could never hope to detect its motion with our crude experiments."

Galileo refused to become a slave to his own experiments. He knew that there were times when a scientist need not accept experimentation as final.

Fifty years later Ole Roemer, the Danish astronomer, using a distance not of a few miles but of 186,000,000 miles discovered that light travels at the tremendous speed of 186,000 miles per second. Galileo would have been pleased to know that Roemer made his discovery after timing the eclipses of one of the moons of Jupiter.

In the late summer of 1638 a traveler from a far country called on Galileo. He was the young English poet John Milton. At that time little known, he was to become one of the greatest writers in the world.

"I have come all the way from England to see you," Milton said.

"You come at a bad time," Galileo responded. "You see before you a blind old man, deserted by the world and spied on by his enemies. The universe which I enlarged a hundred, nay a thousand, times is now shrunk for me within the bounds of my own fingertips."

"But your eyes," Milton cried, "have seen more than all the sons of Adam since the beginning of time. The day will come when the things you have seen will be known to all men throughout the earth."

"How can men know what I have discovered?" said Galileo sorrowfully. "Here in my own beloved country, my books may not be reprinted. If I write a book, I cannot get permission to publish it. Day after day I must bear the insults of those who know far less than I. Yet I may never raise my voice in my own defense. How foolish I was to think that I alone could change the age-old opinions of the universities and of the Church. How vain to imagine that I could give mankind a more glorious view of God's blessed universe. I have lost everything and science has returned to the dark ages before Copernicus. Galileo Galilei is already forgotten as though he had never lived."

"But you are not forgotten," Milton protested. "We

know that you are the prisoner of the Inquisition. We know how much you have suffered for your love of the truth. Wherever there is freedom to speak and write, your books are read and praised. Throughout Europe, openly and secretly, scientists are studying what you have taught. Nightly the stars are scanned with the telescope you invented. Do not fear. The lamp of knowledge you have lighted is not so easily put out. Even the Church that today turns her face from you will some day hail you as one of her most glorious sons."

Caught up by the young man's hope for the future, Galileo began to smile.

"Spoken like a true poet," he said. "My work is a beginning, a means by which other minds brighter than mine will explore all the corners of this vast and most excellent universe. Perhaps my work has not been altogether in vain. At all events I put up a good fight."

Galileo was right. On Christmas Day of the year he died, 1642, a child named Isaac Newton was born in England. He was destined to carry to a glorious victory the work Galileo Galilei had so nobly begun.

Chapter 19 / Four Hundred
Years After

T<small>HE</small> <small>FIRST</small> <small>MAN</small> to look upon the true face of the moon, to see the earth clearly as one of the planets of the solar system and to chart stars of whose existence mankind had never dreamed, Galileo Galilei swung open the gates to a vast universe whose bounds still remain to be explored.

Within the space of a few short months in 1610 Galileo learned more about the true nature of the heavens than had been known in all previous time. The astronauts who land on the moon tomorrow will owe him a debt for the very first map of the lunar surface he designed a little less than four hundred years ago.

Galileo's greatness lies not in the chance fact that he possessed a device that could explore the sky at close hand. In his hands the telescope was more than an instrument for plotting constellations, detecting the phases of Venus or counting the moons of Jupiter. For him it became a way of solving some of the fundamental problems of the strange and awesome world into which we are born. Once Galileo had looked through his telescope, our planet, formerly conceived as the center of the universe, could take its proper size and place within the immensity and grandeur of the cosmos.

His extraordinary genius was equally at home with events that happen right under our noses as well as events occurring far out in space. The rate of fall of a stone aroused his curiosity as much as the appearance of a new star in the sky. The planets are subject to the very same forces that apply to balls rolling down an inclined plane. Earth and heaven are part of one grand design, all subject to the same universal laws.

At the time he challenged the old system of the universe, Galileo realized he had to create a new science of motion to replace that of Aristotle. The new astronomy demanded a new physics and in *The Two New Sciences* he offered a demonstration of how the new sciences operated. As keenly alert as any modern physicist to observing, experimenting and analyzing results, he nevertheless placed his basic faith in mathematical reasoning. He began his career as a mathematician and for him, mathematics was always the queen of the sciences. "The book of the universe," he once wrote, "is written in mathematical language whose alphabet consists of triangles, circles, and geometric figures." His laws of falling bodies could never have been formulated on the basis of experiment alone since, as the professors were quick to point out, feathers certainly do not fall at the same speed as metal balls. He dared to reason that in a vacuum objects would fall according to the laws he had discovered. The great experimenter was willing to venture into areas where experiment was of no use to him.

One thing often overlooked about Galileo is his literary ability. Using the common language of the people at a time when all learned men were communicating in Latin, he expressed his ideas in an easily understood style that still makes exciting reading.

The first publicist for science, he deliberately set out to be entertaining and amusing. Science was so clear to him he saw no reason why it should not be equally clear to the reader. *The Starry Messenger* is full of interest and suspense. Through January and February of 1610 Galileo shares every night with the reader as he turns "Old Discoverer" toward the heavens, picking up the starlets that have arranged themselves in such a curious straight line with Jupiter and speculating as to their true nature. You wonder what the next night will bring as the stars change their position. At last breathing a sigh of relief you realize that these "stars" are really satellites circling the great planet. When you open the pages of *The Two Chief World Systems* you enter into the argument, join in the process of reasoning and fight it out along with Salviati, Sagredo and Simplicio.

In an age of mass conformity when all men accepted without question what the old writers had taught, Galileo challenged blind belief in authority. At a time when everyone thought that all the questions had already been asked and all the answers given, he urged his students to say, "I do not know." A fierce antagonist, giving no quarter and expecting none, Galileo tore into his enemies with glee and sent them flying from the field. Only when shielded by the cloak of the Inquisition did they dare to return.

The greatest struggle in Galileo's life was not with his enemies, fierce as the combat was, but with himself. Deeply attached to his religion, Galileo considered himself a true son of the Church all his life. Yet he could not deny the scientific convictions that led him step by step into a conflict he never intended. Why did he not flee when the dreaded summons came from Rome? He could easily have found refuge in Republican Venice or Protestant Holland. The answer is that he never ceased to acknowledge the final authority of his Church over his soul.

Because Galileo's discoveries have become in our time the commonplaces of science, it is hard to imagine how they could have aroused so much passion and caused so much suffering. We cannot understand why intelligent men balked at accepting them until we realize that they seemed to violate not only religious doctrine but also good common sense.

"To say," said Cardinal Bellarmine, "that the sun does not travel from east to west in the heavens and that the earth moves about the sun not only injures our faith and calls the Bible false but also is contrary to common sense. Doesn't our eye show us each day that the sun does move through the heavens?"

To all this Galileo could only respond with closely reasoned scientific arguments most people impatiently rejected. It was as difficult for them to accept the new scheme of the universe as it would be for us today to accept theirs.

Galileo's life reminds us that what we so easily take for granted was bitterly fought for. Recognition of many of the scientific laws that are so neatly listed for us in a physics or astronomy text was achieved only because brave men were willing to suffer and die. Between the lines we see Giordano Bruno being burned at the stake or Galileo Galilei in the white shirt of the penitent being led through the streets of the Eternal City to his final humiliation.

Galileo's battle to transform physics into an exact science has been won. But the battle against bigotry and ignorance goes on, waged by men who dare to speak up no matter how great the odds against them.

When the sightless Galileo died at Arcetri on January 8, 1642, Urban VIII forbade the erection of a monument in his honor by the Grand Duke of Tuscany lest any word on it offend the reputation of the Holy Office. Yet today Church, State and Science honor the memory of the man who stood alone against the world.

THE PEOPLE IN THIS STORY are real men and women whose conversation wherever possible has been taken from their letters and from what their contemporaries said about them. Since very little is known about the details of Galileo's early life, I have taken the liberty of creating several fictitious characters: Father Orsini, the abbot of the monastery of Vallombrosa that Galileo attended as a boy; his teacher Brother Paolo; Galileo's bumbling student at Padua, "my good Corsi"; and Brother Sarpi's efficient bodyguard. But the professors are real, every one of them.

Galileo's Works

Dialogue Concerning the Two Chief World Systems, Ptolemaic and Copernican, Translated by Stillman Drake. New York: Berkeley, 1953.

Discoveries and Opinions of Galileo, Edited by Stillman Drake. New York: Doubleday Anchor Books, 1957.

> An excellent introduction to Galileo's own writing, including *The Starry Messenger, Letters on Sun spots,* and excerpts from *The Assayer.*

Books About Galileo

The Crime of Galileo by Giorgio De Santillana. Chicago: University of Chicago Press, 1955.

> Far and away the most readable and knowledgeable biography of Galileo published in recent years, stressing the later events in his life.

Galileo, His Life and Work by J. H. Fahie. London: John Murray, 1903.

Background Reading

A History of Astronomy from Thales to Kepler by John L. E. Dreyer. New York: Dover, 1953.

A Short History of Science by W. T. Sedgwick and H. W. Tyler. New York: Macmillan, 1960.

A Short History of Science and Scientific Thought by F. Sherwood Taylor. New York: W. W. Norton, 1949.

Events in Galileo's Life		*World Events*
Born in Pisa	1564	Birth of William Shakespeare
		Death of Michelangelo
	1571	Turks defeated at Battle of Lepanto
Began studies at Vallombrosa	1577	Sir Francis Drake began round-the-world voyage
Entered University of Pisa; discovered law of uniformity of pendulum swing and invented pulse timer	1581	Netherlands declared independence from Spain
	1582	New Gregorian calendar adopted by Italy, Spain, Portugal and France
	1588	Defeat of Spanish Armada by England
Became Professor at University of Pisa	1589	
Appointed Professor of Mathematics at University of Padua	1592	
	1598	Birth of Oliver Cromwell
		Henry IV of France issued Edict of Nantes, guaranteeing religious freedom to Huguenots
Birth of daughter Virginia	1600	
Birth of daughter Livia	1601	
	1603	Death of Queen Elizabeth I of England
Announced discovery of laws of falling bodies and allegiance to Copernican theory	1604	

	1605	Death of Mogul Emperor Akbar the Great; publication of Francis Bacon's *On the Advancement of Learning*
Published book on the military compass; birth of son Vincenzio	1606	
	1607	Founding of Jamestown colony in Virginia
Invented telescope; awarded lifetime professorship at University of Padua	1609	Kepler announced discovery of laws of planetary motion
Publication of *The Starry Messenger*, Venice; returned to Florence	1610	
Publication of *Letters on Sun Spots*, Rome	1613	
	1615	*Don Quixote* completed by Cervantes
Copernican theory banned by the Church	1616	Death of William Shakespeare
	1618	Beginning of Thirty Years' War in Europe
	1620	Founding of Plymouth colony in New England
	1622	Birth of Molière
Publication of *The Assayer, Discourse on Comets*, Rome	1623	
	1625	Settlement of New Amsterdam, later New York
	1628	Publication of William Harvey's *Concerning the Movement of the Heart*

Publication of *The Two Chief World Systems*, Florence	1632	Death of King Gustavus Adolphus of Sweden in battle of Lützen
Imprisonment by the Inquisition and renunciation of belief in Copernican theory, Rome	1633	
Death of daughter Sister Maria Celeste	1634	
Striken by blindness	1637	Descartes' *Discours de la Méthode* published
Publication of *The Two New Sciences*, Leyden	1638	
Death in Arcetri	1642	Birth of Isaac Newton